A LINE–FORMULA
CHEMICAL NOTATION

QV4QV

A LINE–FORMULA
CHEMICAL NOTATION

QV4QV

WILLIAM J. WISWESSER

Head of Industrial Hygiene and Chemical Research
Willson Products, Inc., Reading, Pennsylvania

THOMAS Y. CROWELL COMPANY
New York – 1954

53593

MANUFACTURED IN THE UNITED STATES OF AMERICA
BY THE PLIMPTON PRESS, NORWOOD, MASSACHUSETTS

FOREWORD

The history of science is filled with instances where new understandings have developed from the introduction of new techniques. From the air pump to the cyclotron the advance of scientific knowledge has depended upon such invention to provide new data to facilitate man's understanding and control of the world around him. A new technique may also provide fresh ways of looking at old data and a truly powerful technique, of whatever sort, often finds use in ways its inventor never could have foreseen.

Here is just such a new technique for handling data about chemical compounds. It is a new chemical notation by which even complicated chemical structures may be expressed concisely and without ambiguity in a single line of letters, numbers and punctuation marks. It has been designed to provide a straightforward way of indexing chemical compounds and so to bypass the present growing confusions and frustrations in chemical nomenclature. How many chemists today can confidently name, unassisted, a very complex molecule they may have synthesized or for which they may wish to search the literature? My own personal experience in coding some seven thousand organic compounds into this notation (in connection with a catalog of physical properties) has convinced me that it does this indexing job well. The encoding process is simple and logical and the resulting notation is clear and recognizable, all without recourse to books of codes, lists showing precedence of groups, or other such devices. Moreover, as Dr. Frederic Benson demonstrated at the national meeting of the American Chemical Society in Chicago in 1954, the notation can be successfully searched for structural components in a variety of ways on punched card machinery equipped with multiple-column scanning devices.

This new technique in chemical notation is partly a development of the pioneering work of Dr. Dyson, Dr. Gruber, and others, partly a bold application of certain fundamental principles which have been in daily use for a long time in the accepted chemical nomenclature and partly the systematic application of a new principle first put forward by Mr. Wiswesser. This principle is the resolution of possible notations for a given structure on the simple basis of the position of the symbols in the alphabet. This principle, combined with Mr. Wiswesser's careful choice of a few new symbols to supplement the old familiar ones, at once does away with lengthy, arbitrary and confusing lists showing the precedence of groups, the bugbear of most notations, and is one of those strokes of genius which seem in retrospect to be such plain common sense that one wonders why he didn't think of it himself! Mr. Wiswesser, however, not only did think of it but has had the tenacity and courage to work it out in great detail in the comprehensive notation described in this book.

This notation may well have other ramifications in the illumination it sheds on old ways of doing things. For example, it becomes apparent in studying the notation procedures for complex cyclic compounds discussed near the end of the book, that the old ring nomenclatures have largely ignored what now seem, topologically, the most important ring positions of all — the positions where the rings are joined!

Chemists generally seem aware that future progress in communication and utilization of chemical knowledge will require some sort of new chemical notation. Mr. Wiswesser's contribution to that end deserves the earnest attention of all who are interested in that advance.

ELBERT G. SMITH
Associate Professor of Chemistry
The University of Hawaii

PREFACE

This manual is the culmination of a long search for a chemical notation that should consist of symbols limited to those on the standard typewriter keyboard. The necessity for such a notation has been made almost inescapable by recent tremendous advances in technology and the vast growth of chemical literature.

During the past few years the author has tried to perfect this notation by seeking opinions of others, absorbing their criticism, and accumulating data. He has insofar as possible avoided novelty where past practices could be followed. In fact, he has followed the spirit of the statement made by the editors of the First Decennial Index of *Chemical Abstracts:*

> "Our aim has been to follow existing usage as far as it could be made fairly consistent, choosing what appeared to us good practices and rejecting bad, and introducing new features only when some very positive advantage was to be gained." — Patterson and Curran, *J. Am. Chem. Soc.* 39, 1623–38 (1917)

In this notation, therefore, those familiar methods that require the least writing, and the least new learning, and the least memorizing have been given strict preference.

The rules of procedure have been carefully developed in order to give one and only one correct sequence of symbols for each chemical compound. The rules have been numbered so as to emphasize their logical associations; for example, the pattern in Rules 1, 2, and 3 is repeated in Rules 11, 12, and 13. Rules 20 and 30 are fundamental for cyclic structures more complex than benzene rings. Sets of review exercises are included to aid the reader in learning the notation. Answers are provided for all the problems in the first few chapters as well as for subsequent "encoding" questions.

This manual in its entirety is an acknowledgment of gratitude to the scores of friends and correspondents who volunteered their ideas, opinions, and time in the common effort to develop a workable notation. In addition, specific acknowledgment must be made to Frederic L. Benson, Howard T. Bonnett, Wolfgang Gruber, Lester E. Kuentzel, Philip A. Sadtler, Elbert G. Smith, and Kenneth S. Warren, who helped to demonstrate or explore the practical advantages of this notation; to Aaron Addelston, George E. Brewer, Edward M. Crane, Cyrus G. Dunkle, Robert A. Hardy, Jr., Charles A. Heiberger, Donald Hill, A. F. Isbell, J. J. Leavitt, J. Scott Maclennan, Herman Skolnik, and Donald M. Sundland, who wrote or spoke so eloquently for the notation-testing A.C.S. Volunteers; to Ann Weik, E. D. Amstutz, James F. Feeman, George Garcelon, Roy W. Hamme, Roderick Horning, and C. S. Sherman, who checked various sections of the manuscript, the review exercises, or the index; to Stanley G. Brooker, John Conway, Stanley A. Hall, Sidney Kasman, Harold P. Klug, Franz Leiss, Charles R. Maxwell, A. D. Mitchell, Alexander M. Moore, Howard Nechamkin, Milton Schechter, Sir John Simonsen, H. H. Schrenk, Henry F. Smyth, Jr., F. Lowell Taylor, and Frederick Y. Wiselogle, who gave valuable advice or welcome encouragement during the critical period of the past five years; and to Mary Alexander, Madeline Berry, Harriet A. Geer, Mildred Grafflin, Paul Arthur, Jr., Charles L. Bernier, William F. Bruce, G. Malcolm Dyson, M. Gordon, Lewis Hess, Karl F. Heumann, Walter R. Kirner, Stanley P. Klesney, Howard S. Nutting, Austin M. Patterson, James W. Perry, Eugene W. Scott, and J. A. Silk, who offered challenging and constructive criticisms in the early stages of the development of this notational.

WILLIAM J. WISWESSER

April, 1954

CONTENTS

Part One

THE SYSTEM OF SYMBOLS

Part Two

ALIPHATIC (OPEN–CHAIN) COMPOUNDS

Part Three

CYCLIC COMPOUNDS

Part One

THE SYSTEM OF SYMBOLS

1

THE INTERNATIONAL ATOMIC SYMBOLS

Chemical notation is a *system of symbols* — numerals, letters, and marks — designed to indicate the structures of molecules. The word "system" in this definition has important logical implications: well-chosen symbols should be obvious in meaning, easy to use, and easy to write or type or print; they should give concise and instantly recognizable structure descriptions that are neat in appearance and precise in meaning. These qualities are prerequisite to the further requirement of notational uniqueness — of citing the symbols in such a specific order that one and only one sequence will be recognized as correct for each structure (see Chapter 4). Thus the selection of symbols requires considerable thought and care in order best to meet these general considerations and those emphasized in the following section, "Logical Sets of Symbols."

The first characteristic feature of this notation is that the atomic symbols are cited in a pictorially direct and self-evident *connecting order*, as shown in the following descriptions of lineal molecular structures: FCCF, FOF, NCCN, NCHgCN, NCSCN, NCSSCN, OCO, ONO, ONONO, OSO, SCCCS, and SCS.

The second characteristic feature is that asymmetric "forward or backward" sequences of symbols are resolved through their self-evident *alphabetic order*. In the sense that "forward" has higher alphabetic rank than the word "backward," the *highest-ranking* * *sequence is the preferred one* for lineal structures: FSOF, ICCF, IF,

* The last letters — Z, Y, X, etc., — in an alphabet have highest rank, in analogy with the definition that the first numbers 1, 2, 3, etc., in a counting sequence have lowest numeric value. (Vertical lists of symbols show a physical "low-to-high" correspondence only when arranged in the "bottom-to-top" order.)

NCF, NCSF, NNNCN, OC, ON, ONN, ONSCN, SCO, and SO. Isolated single unsaturations are indicated with an interposed colon mark, as in O:AsF, O:NF, O:NOF, and S:PF.

The third characteristic feature is that branched-chain structures always are described in a *rightward*-unfolding direction; that is, the "side group" symbols always follow (rather than precede) the symbol of the "main chain" atom to which they are attached. These and other features relating to structural branches, rings, and the like, will be understood more readily after all of the systematic atomic group symbols have been introduced, since these same symbols yield lucid *graphical diagrams* when cited in two-dimensional branched arrays.

LOGICAL SETS OF SYMBOLS

The fundamental aim in this development of a systematic notation is the reduction of all learning, remembering, writing, and thinking effort to a practical minimum. The learning and remembering effort is minimized by using the traditional chemical symbols and "line-formula" delineating method as much as possible, for these traditional habits usually represent long-enduring majority preferences. The writing effort is minimized by using single-mark symbols for those structural units (atoms and simple radicals) that occur *very frequently* in the general chemical literature. The thinking effort is minimized by fully "spelling out" all of the rarer atoms and atomic groups, and particularly by employing logical sets of symbols.

This fundamental aim dictates four general propositions on the over-all selection of symbols:

1. Reserve capitalized letter symbols to denote atoms or atomic groups.

2. Reserve punctuation marks to denote modes of connection or disconnection.

3. Reserve numeric symbols to denote *absolute* numerical measures, such as the number of skeletal atoms in a ring or in an alkyl chain.

4. Reserve lower-case letters (rather than numbers) as locants * to locate *relative* ring positions.

These four propositions also have a clear historical justification. Thus capitalized letter symbols have been reserved to denote atoms

---

* Dr. G. M. Dyson in 1947 popularized the word *locant*, meaning a positional designation.

and simple radicals ever since 1789, when William Higgins wrote: "Let S be a particle of sulfur," "Let I be iron"; "Let C be copper," and so on.[*] Hassenfratz and Adet [†] at that same time introduced the practice of using a second (lower-case) letter for further distinction, such as their encircled semialchemistic symbol As to denote *the presence of* arsenic (their encircled A denoted the presence of silver or "argentum"). Half a century later organic chemists used similar pairs of letters to denote *groups* of atoms, such as Bz for the benzoyl radical (Liebig and Wohler), and Ac for the acetyl radical (Liebig, 1839).

Periods, commas, and hyphens have been used for almost a century (Loschmidt, 1861; Hübner, 1862; Carius, 1863; Hofmann, 1865; Buff, Debus, and Kekulé, 1866) to "set off" the successive segments of atomic groups in a line-formula description, or to "terminate" segments having side groups. Colons were used to denote ethylenic unsaturations soon after the corresponding "double-bond" valence lines appeared (Erlenmeyer, 1866). Thus all of these punctuation marks have been reserved to denote modes of connection or disconnection in the structure descriptions.

Numerals have been used for more than half a century to denote the number of members or skeletal atoms in ring structures. These numerals have been printed as boldface figures in the Ring Index, which is a part of the general guide to *Chemical Abstracts*, for each year since 1916; however, the boldface type is not necessary and is not used in text copy. In the notation proposed in this manual, these *ring numerals* are enclosed distinctively in parentheses, along with other symbols that complete the description of the ring system; thus the same numerals, outside the parentheses, serve as ideal single-mark descriptions of the corresponding short *alkyl chains*, the commonest of all structural units.

Lower-case letters were used by Kekulé in 1866 [‡] to identify the six substituting positions in the hexagonal benzene ring (a to f); and to itemize the corresponding possible sets of uniformly substituted products (bisubstituted ab, ac, ad; trisubstituted abc, abd, ace; tetrasubstituted $abcd$, $abce$, $abde$; etc.). These distinctive lower-case letters are more concise than numerals to locate ring positions

[*] Higgins, "A Comparative View of the Phlogistic and Antiphlogistic Theories," 2nd ed., Oxford, London, 1791, pages 39, 48, 59, 262.

[†] Hassenfratz and Adet, "New System of Chymical Characters" (an English appendix to "Méthode de Nomenclature Chimique," by Guyton de Morveau, Lavoisier, Bertholet, and de Fourcroy, Paris, 1787).

[‡] A. Kekulé, *Annalen der Chemie und Pharmacie*, **137,** 158 (1866).

because a single mark, without punctuation, suffices for values up to the 26th position; and structures requiring locants beyond this value (shown with prime marks) are very rare indeed.*

FAMILIAR ATOMIC SYMBOLS

The well-established international atomic symbols B, C, F, H, I, N, O, P, and S, being ultimates in brevity to denote single atoms of these 9 nonmetallic elements, are retained *without any alteration in meaning.* Similarly, 81 of the 83 well-established two-letter symbols are retained without change because only chlorine and bromine occur frequently enough in the literature to justify any shorter symbol. Conversely, 6 of the 15 elements now denoted by single-letter symbols (A, K, U, V, W, and Y) occur so rarely in large listings that this inefficient use of 6 of the 26 capital-letter symbols is open to question. Greater logical consistency also can be gained by having single-letter symbols for the 8 most electronegative elements (fluorine, oxygen, nitrogen, chlorine, bromine, carbon, sulfur, and iodine), and two-letter symbols for the 86 least electronegative elements (the symbols Se, H, P, and B for the intervening 4 elements being retained). Thus 90 of the 98 international atomic symbols are retained to denote single atoms of these elements, without any loss in conciseness or in logical consistency.

Table 1 shows how these established atomic symbols are used in a simple and familiar manner to denote fundamental chain-forming groups — terminal radicals and connective radicals. Note that the H-atom symbol always *follows* the principal symbol, in accordance with the original line-formula convention (see Chapter 2). This logical subordination of the least important symbol gives initial *alphabetizing* emphasis in terminal hydride groups to rarer atoms, such as As, Bi, Ge, Sb, Se, Si, Sn, or Te. Note also the general avoidance of subscripts, for ease of printing and typewriting. The "free valence" lines merely denote the direction of attachment to other groups; hence, unlike the colon, these lines are not a part of the complete structure descriptions. (For example, the cyano group must be shown either as a NC— prefix or as a —CN suffix, to distinguish it from the isocyano CN— or —NC group; but the cyanogen molecule is described simply as NCCN.)

* Additional notes on the frequency of appearance in chemical literature of various structural components, and on the history of chemical notation, are given in Appendix A, pages 123–32.

Table 1. FUNDAMENTAL FUNCTIONS DENOTED
WITH FAMILIAR SYMBOLS

Ag—	[Argento]	O:	Oxo (Aldo only)
—AsH—	(Acyl)arsido *	—PH—	(Acyl)phosphido
AsHH—	Arsino	PHH—	Phosphino
Au—	Auro	(PH₄—	Phosphoranyl *)
/		S→	(Acyl)thioyl *
—Au	Auri	—S—	Sulfido †
\		S:	Thiono *
BiHH—	Bismuthino	—SbH—	(Acyl)stibido *
—BH—	(Acyl)borido *	SbHH—	Stibino
BHH—	Borino †	Se→	(Acyl)selenoyl *
C(:)	[Carbyl]	—Se—	Selenido †
F—	Fluoro	Se:	Selenono *
GeHHH—	[Germanyl]	SeH—	Selenyl
—H	[Hydro, Proto]	—SiHH—	Silylene
—Hg—	Mercuri	SiHHH—	Silyl
I—	Iodo	SnHHH—	Stannyl
—N:	(Acyl)imido †	SH—	Mercapto(alkyl)
	or (Alkyl)imino		or Thiolo(acyl)*
N⇌	Nitrido(acyl) *	—Te—	Tellurido *
N(C)—	Nitrilo	Te:	Tellurono *
O→	(Acyl)inyl, onyl *	TeH—	[Telluryl]
—O—	Oxy †		

* Based on proposed new phosphorus nomenclature; see *Chem. Eng. News*, **30**, 4515 (1952).

† Name is taken from the *C.A.* list of "Inorganic Groups and Radicals"; see *C.A.*, **39**, 5956 (1945). All of the remaining unbracketed names are taken from the "List of Radical Names" recommended by the International Union of Pure and Applied Chemistry (IUPAC) at their Amsterdam meeting (September, 1949). See *C.A.*, **46**, 12413 (1952).

The radicals are listed in their ascending alphabetic order of rank — "argento" to "telluryl" — as determined by the symbols.

The colon mark is used to denote isolated "ethylenic" unsaturations that can be hydrogenated, and thus distinguish these double-bond linkages from "dative" bonds (which may be regarded as polarized single-bond linkages). This distinction emphasizes the useful valence generalization that, apart from dative bonds (shown by an arrow in Tables 1 and 4), the halogens generally form *mono*-valent derivatives, the atoms in the sulfur group generally form *bi*valent derivatives, and those in the phosphorus group generally form *tri*valent derivatives.

Table 2 shows how the fundamental chain-forming symbols are cited in a pictorially direct manner (without the single-valence lines), *atom by atom as connected*, to denote compound chain radicals. Doubly unsaturated groups, such as CN—, CNO—, CNS—, NC—,

NCO—, NCS—, NNN—, OCN—, and SCN—, are concisely indicated, easily described, and instantly recognized when coded as shown, without unsaturation marks. Resonance chemists will appreciate a further advantage in not having to infer any theoretically

Table 2. COMPOUND RADICALS DENOTED
WITH FAMILIAR SYMBOLS

AsHHO—	Arsinoxy *	O:As—	Oxoarsino *
—As:As—	Arseno	O:B—	Oxoborino *(Boryl)
—CC—	Ethynylene	O:BO—	Metaborato †
CN—	Isocyano	O:C:	Carbonyl(ene)
CNO—	[Fulminoxy]	O:GeH—	Oxogermanyl *
FO—	[Fluoroxy]	O:N—	Nitroso
IO—	Iod*ino*xy *	O:P—	Oxophosphino *
IPH—	Iodophosphino *	O:Sb—	Oxostibino *
NC—	Cyano	O:SnH—	Oxostannyl *
NCO—	Cyanato	PHHO—	Phosphinoxy *
NCPH—	Cyanophosphino *	—P:As—	Phospharseno
NCS—	Thiocyanato	—P:N—	Phosphazo
:NN:	Azino	—P:P—	Phosphoro
NNN—	Azido	—Sb:As—	Stibarseno
NPH—	Phosphononitridyl *	—Sb:Sb—	Antimono
—N:N—	Azo (Diazo)	SiHHHO—	Siloxy
N:N:	Diazo(alkyl)	SiHHHOSiHH—	Disiloxanyl
OAsHH—	Arsonyl *	SiHHHSiHH—	Disilanyl
OAsHHO—	Arsonyloxy *	SAsHH—	Arsonothioyl *
OAsHHS—	Arsonylsulfido *	SCN—	Isothiocyanato
OCN—	Isocyanato	SHAsH—	Thioloarsino *
—OHg—	[Oxymercuri]	SHPH—	Thiolophosphino *
OI—	Iodinyl *	—SO—	Sulfidoxy
ONN:	Nitrosimino	SPHH—	Phosphonothioyl *
ONO—	Nitrito †	SSbHH—	Stibonothioyl *
—OO—	Peroxy †	—SS—	Disulfido
OPHH—	Phosphonyl *	—SSS—	Trisulfido
OSbHH—	Stibonyl *	S:As—	Thionoarsino *
OSeH—	Seleninyl *	S:C:	Thiocarbonyl(ene)
OSH—	Sulfinyl *	S:P—	Thionophosphino *
OTeH—	Tellurinyl *	S:Sb—	Thionostibino *

* Based on proposed new phosphorus nomenclature in *Chem. Eng. News*, **30**, 4515 (1952), except that the letter *o* is used instead of *i* to denote *maximum valence or coordination of the central atom.*

† Name is taken from the *C.A.* list of "Inorganic Groups and Radicals." All of the remaining unbracketed names are taken from the IUPAC Amsterdam Report.

objectionable postulations about multiple bonds in these polyatomic groups. Therefore, none of these groups merit new symbols. If any new symbols are sought to improve the value and versatility of linear descriptions, these "strange new symbols" should be so few in number and so frequent in application that they are universally appealing — easy to learn, easy to remember, and easy if not inviting to use.

Table 3 shows how the *graphically branched* combinations of familiar symbols are delineated in a systematic manner — and in full accord with the traditional line-formula convention. Although every monovalent group begins with a terminal symbol, note that *only one* such symbol can precede the first branched-atom symbol; all "side-group" symbols, like the H-atom symbol, must *follow* the branched-atom symbols. Thus the correct sequence of symbols for the cyanofluorophosphino radical is NCPF—, not NCFP—. The implied difference between NCPS,F—, and NCSPF— should be even more obvious.

Table 3. PHYSICALLY BRANCHED GROUPS DENOTED WITH FAMILIAR SYMBOLS

—AsHS.—	-Arsonothioyl *	OPHF—	Fluorophosphonyl *
FPF—	Difluorophosphino *	—PS,F—	-Fluorophosphonothioyl *
IAsF—	Fluoroiodoarsino *	—SeO.—	-Seleninyl
NCAsHS.—	Cyanoarsonothioyl †	SAsFF—	Difluoroarsonothioyl *
NCAsO,F—	Cyanofluoroarsonyl †	SAsHI.—	Iodoarsonothioyl *
NCPHO.—	Cyanophosphonyl †	SAsS.—	Thionoarsonothioyl *
—NO:N—	-Azoxy (nonspecific O)	SHPHO.—	Thiolophosphonyl *
OPFF—	Difluorophosphonyl *	SHSbHS.—	Thiolostibonothioyl †
—PHO.—	-Phosphonyl *	—SO.—	-Sulfinyl
—PN.—	-Phosphono-nitridyl	SPO.—	Thioxophosphoyl *

* Based on proposed new phosphorus nomenclature (see *Chem. Eng. News*, **30**, 4515, 1952), except that the letter *o* is used instead of *i* to denote maximum valence or coordination of the central atom.

† In these cases, note that the *longest* sequence of marks (letters, colons, and numerals if any) does not begin with the highest-ranking terminal sequence. Note the alphabetic order of rank (Rule 2a, page 33), the "longest symbol sequence" orientation (Rule 3a, page 34), and the subordination of the H-atom symbol (Rule 6a, page 45).

The systematic delineation is discussed more fully in Chapter 4, since the problem of properly "compounding" the symbols naturally should be deferred until all of the "elementary" symbols have been introduced.

REVIEW EXERCISES

1. Convert the following covalent inorganic formula "descriptions" to systematic line-formula notations; specify unsaturations only when necessary to avoid ambiguity.

boron trifluoride, BF_3

diiodoacetylene, C_2I_2

nitric oxide, NO

nitrosyl fluoride, (NO)F

nitrous anhydride, N_2O_3

nitrous oxide, N_2O

phosphoryl fluoride, POF_3

sulfur monofluoride, S_2F_2

2. Give the systematic notations for the unbranched dioxides of carbon, iodine, nitrogen, oxygen (O_3), selenium, and sulfur.

3. Convert the following carbon-containing compound descriptions to systematic notations:

1-azido-2-cyano-acetylene, $C_2(N_3)CN$

carbon disulfide, CS_2

carbon monoxide, CO

carbon oxysulfide, COS

carbon suboxide, C_3O_2

carbon subsulfide, C_3S_2

cyanoacetylene, $C_2(CN)_2$

cyanogen, C_2N_2

cyanogen sulfide, $S(CN)_2$

cyanogen disulfide, $S_2(CN)_2$

4. Distinguish between the following pairs of isomers with valence-line structure diagrams:

CNCCNC   vs.   NCCCCN   NCSSCN   vs.   SNCCNS

FSSF   vs.   SSFF   OPFFF   vs.   FPFOF

Answers:

1. FBFF, ICCI, ON, ONF, ONONO, ONN, OPFFF, and FSSF.

2. OCO, OIO, ONO, OOO, OSeO, OSO.

3. NNNCCCN, SCS, OC, SCO, OCCCO, SCCCS, NCCCCN, NCCN, NCSCN, NCSSCN.

4. Hints: Show single coordinate links (arrows) in SSFF and OPFFF, double bonds in SNCCNS.

2

NEW ATOMIC GROUP SYMBOLS

Fortunately, 81 of the 83 presently established two-letter atomic symbols (all but Br and Cl) are met so rarely in the literature that these may be retained without change, as previously mentioned. The six rarely used one-letter atomic symbols A, K, U, V, W, and Y are replaced by two-letter symbols, Ar, Ka, Ur, Vd, Wf, and Yt, thereby improving their recognition or discrimination with automatic scanning machinery and releasing these single letters to denote certain important and frequently met groups. Nine single-letter atomic symbols (B, C, F, H, I, N, O, P, and S) are retained, but the four most frequently used symbols (H, C, O, and N) are restricted in order to improve the recognizability, conciseness, and sorting efficiency of their fundamental intercombinations. These basic selections and modifications of the established letter symbols are summarized in the outline given at the end of Chapter 3.

TEN NEW SPECIFIC LETTER SYMBOLS

Ten new capital-letter symbols have been selected to denote seven prominent chain-forming groups (E, G, M, Q, V, W, and Z), which are logically related to the other fundamental letter symbols, as shown in Tables 4 and 5, and three prominent branch-forming groups (Y, X, and K), which are similarly illustrated in Tables 6 and 7. These ten specific letter symbols for open-chain structural segments are readily mastered when associated with the following mnemonic learning aids, given as definitions:

Halogen Atoms

G (from *haloGen*), the 7th letter of the alphabet (and following F for fluorine), denotes an atom of chlorine, the most prominent

Group 7 element. (The objectionable typewriting ambiguity in Cl also should be noted.)

E (from *halogEn*), lowest in the alphabetic sequence of halogen symbols or names, denotes an atom of bromine.

Thus GSG is sulfur dichloride; GSSG, sulfur monochloride; and OGO, chlorine dioxide. Similarly, NCE is cyanogen bromide and IE, iodine monobromide.

Oxygen Functions

O is reserved to denote the "lone" O-atom segments in alde-hydes and ketenes (with colon); or in ethers, esters, —SO.—, —PHO.—, etc., groups (without colon).

Q (from *aQua*) denotes the —OH group, literally an O atom with a proton "tail."

V (Very common diValent connectiVe) denotes the *keto*-carbonyl —C(:O)— group. This symbol is not used for either the *keteno* O:C: or the *aldo* O: terminal groups, which are denoted with colons and other letters as shown here.

W (double O) denotes the nonlinear "dioxo" or O_2 group, as in the nitro —NO_2 and sulfonyl —SO_2— radicals. It is not used for *lineal* or 2-coordinate structures such as OCO, OGO, ONO, and OSO.

Thus QH denotes water; QQ, hydrogen peroxide; and QG, hypochlorous acid. Similarly, QVQ denotes carbonic acid; QVVQ, oxalic acid; and GVG, phosgene. Finally, WNF denotes nitryl fluoride; WNQ, nitric acid; and WSQQ, sulfuric acid.

Nitrogen Functions

N is reserved to denote "lone" N atoms as in CN—, NC—, —N:N—, WN—, or tertiary amino groups.

M (from *iMino* or *Mid-aMino*), a letter larger than N but closely associated with it, denotes the NH group (a terminal M: or connective —M— or ionic M).

Z (from *hydraZine*), terminal in the alphabet and pictorially like the letter N "on end," denotes the —NH_2 group of amines, amides, and the like.

K (from "*Kwaternary*"), a four-stem symbol like X, denotes the fully alkylated and cationic nitrogen atom, quaternary in open chain positions.

Thus NN:M denotes hydrazoic acid; ZCN, cyanamide; ZQ, hydroxylamine; ZVMNW, nitrourea; ZVZ, urea; and ZZ, hydrazine. "Ortho-nitric acid" would be denoted QKQQO.

Table 4. FUNDAMENTAL FUNCTIONS DENOTED
WITH NEW LETTER SYMBOLS

E—	Bromo	M:	Imido(acyl) [†]
G—	Chloro		or Imino(alkyl) :NH
K—	Quaternary N	Q—	Hydroxy OH
—M—	(Acyl)amido [†]	—V—	Keto-carbonyl CO
	or (Alkyl)amino NH	W—	Dioxo (nonlinear)
M→	(Acyl)imyl * NH	Z—	Amido(acyl) *
			or Amino(alkyl) NH_2

Table 5. COMPOUND RADICALS CONTAINING
NEW LETTER SYMBOLS

EV—	[Bromoformyl]	SiHHHM-	Silylamino
FV—	[Fluoroformyl]	SHV—	[Thioloformyl]
GAsHO—	Chloroarsinoxy *	—VV—	Oxalyl
GHg—	Chloromercuri	—VVV—	Mesoxalyl
GM—	[Chloramido]	WAs—	Arso O_2As—
GN:	[Chlorimido]	WI—	"Iodoxy" O_2I—
GO—	[Hypochlorito]	WN—	Nitro O_2N—
GS—	[Chlorosulfido]	WNM—	Nitramino
GV—	[Chloroformyl]	WNO—	Nitrato [†]
IV—	[Iodoformyl]	WP—	Phospho O_2P—
—MM—	Hydrazo NHNH	WPO—	Metaphosphato [†]
—MMVMM-	[Carbohydrazido]	WSb—	Stibo O_2Sb—
MPHH—	Phosphonimyl *	ZAsHO—	Amidoarsinoxy *
—MVM—	Ureylene	ZM—	Hydrazino
—N:NM—	Diazoamino	ZMV—	[Hydrazinoformyl]
OPHHM—	Phosphonylamido *	ZMVMM—	[Carbazido]
O:NM—	Nitrosamino	ZN:	Hydrazono
—OVO—	*Carbonyldioxy*	ZN:N—	Triazeno
—OVVO—	Oxalato [†]	ZO—	[Aminoxy] H_2NO—
QM—	Hydroxyamino	ZPH—	Amidophosphino *
QMV—	[Hydroxyaminoformyl]	ZV—	Carbamoyl
QN:	*Hydroxyimino*	ZVM—	Ureido
QO—	Hydroperoxy [†]	ZVMM—	Semicarbazido
QOV—	[Hydroperoxyformyl]	ZVMN:	Semicarbazono
QPHO—	Hydroxyphosphinoxy *	ZVMV—	[Ureidoformyl]
QV—	Carboxy HOCO.—	ZVV—	Oxamoyl
QVO—	[Hydroxyformyloxy]	ZVVM—	Oxamido

* See first note in Table 1, page 7. New IUPAC preferences are italicized.
[†] See second note in Table 1.

Table 5 illustrates a number of linear combinations of chain-forming radicals described with the seven new functional-group symbols E, G, M, Q, V, W, and Z. At this point the reader will gain a better understanding of these symbols by "decoding" to the conventional line-formula descriptions, and checking the answers through the *Chemical Abstracts* List of Prefix Radicals (revised in the 1952 Index). For example, the ZVMN: (semicarbazono) group can be decoded symbol by symbol to the familiar NH_2—CO.NH—N: line-formula description. These linear sequences of symbols furthermore can be given in reverse order as *suffix* radicals, without losing the pictorial directness. Thus :N—NH—CO.NH_2 is coded directly as a :NMVZ suffix.

Aliphatic Carbon Branches

Y (from Y-forked) denotes the open-chain *ternary* —CH—
|

group in isoalkanes, and the same group in "secondary" alcohols, etc.; or the corresponding unsaturated :C— atom
|

containing one side group other than :O.

X (from X-branched) denotes the open-chain *quaternary* carbon atom in neoalkanes and the isosteric carbon atom in "tertiary" alcohols, etc., wherein the C atom contains two side groups and thus pictorially resembles the aliphatic K symbol for a quaternary nitrogen atom.

Thus, GYGG denotes chloroform; GXGGG, carbon tetrachloride; and WNXGGG, chloropicrin. Graphical diagrams such as those given below "unfold" the physically branched combinations of symbols in a lucid manner:

			G	G
EYE	ZY:M	ZY:S	GY—XG	GXVG
E	Z	Z	G G	G
bromoform	guanidine	thiourea	pentachloro-ethane	trichloracetyl ehloride
EYEE	ZYZ:M	ZYZ:S	GYGXGGG	GXGGVG

Note that all of the structures are delineated systematically by a simple procedure that will be explained more fully in Chapter 2.

Table 6 shows how to indicate physically branched groups containing the new letter symbols, again in the systematic manner that gives one and only one correct sequence for each structure.

Table 6. PHYSICALLY BRANCHED GROUPS
CONTAINING NEW LETTER SYMBOLS

—AsQO—	-Arsinico, —AsO₂H—
—CrW—	-Chromoyl,*—CrO₂—
GXGG—	Trichloromethyl
M:YZ—	Amidino (Guanyl) †
M:YZM—	Guanidino †
QAsQO.—	Arsono, (OH)₂AsO—
QNO.:	*aci*-Nitro (Isonitro)
QSbQO.—	Stibono, (OH)₂SbO.—
QSeO.—	Selenino, (OH)SeO.—
QSO.—	Sulfino, (OH)SO.—
—SbQO.—	Stibinico, —SbO₂H—
—SeW—	-Selenonyl, —SeO₂—
SHPZO.—	Amidothiolophosphonyl †
SHPZS.—	Amidothiolophosphothioyl †
S:YZ—	Thiocarbamoyl †
—SW—	-Sulfonyl, —SO₂—
—VYQV—	-Tartronoyl
WSeQ—	Selenono, O₂Se(OH)—
WSQ—	Sulfo, O₂S(OH)—
WSQM—	Sulfoamino
—Y:M.—	-Imido, —C(:NH)—
—Y:S.—	-Thiocarbonyl, —C(:S)
ZPHO.—	Amidophosphonyl *
ZSW—	Sulfamoyl, NH₂—SO₂—

* Based on proposed new phosphorus nomenclature in *Chem. Eng. News,* **30,** 4515 (1952), except that the letter *o* is used instead of *i* to denote *maximum valence or coordination of the central atom.*

† In these cases, note that the *longest* sequence of letters and colons does not begin with the highest-ranking terminal sequence.

GENERIC LETTER SYMBOLS

A few of the remaining seven letter symbols (A, D, J, L, R, T, and U) are reserved for denoting generic components, such as J for any halo*gen* atom (pronounced with J), A for any alkyl group, and T for any branched atom or group. The symbol Mt is used to denote any metallic atom. The generic letter A (alkyl) concisely describes simple organic structure types, as shown below:

AMA	sec-Amines	NNNA	Azides
ANA.A	tert-Amines	OCNA	Isocyanates
AOA	Ethers	O:A	Aldehydes
AOOA	Peroxides	O:C:A	Ketenes
AOVOA	Carbonates	PHHA	Phosphines
ASA	Sulfides	QA	Alcohols
ASSA	Disulfides	QOA	Hydroperoxides
A;A	Alkenes *	QVA	Carboxylic acids
A;A;A	Alkadienes *	SCNA	Isothiocyanates
A::A	Alkynes	SHA	Mercaptans
AVA	Ketones	SHVA	Thiolic acids
AVOA	Esters	S:A	Thioaldehydes
AVOVA	Anhydrides	WNA	Nitroalkanes
CNA	Isocyanides	ZA	pri-Amines
FA	Fluoroalkanes	ZVA	Amides
GA	Chloroalkanes	ZVAVQ	Amic acids
M:A	Imines	ZVMMA	Semicarbazides
NCA	Nitriles	ZVMVA	Ureides
NCOA	Cyanates	ZVOA	Urethanes
NCSA	Thiocyanates		

* The semicolon indicates a *cis-trans* double bond (see page 20).

Table 7. ORGANIC STRUCTURE TYPES CONTAINING Y- OR X-BRANCHED CARBON ATOMS

(Illustrating the use of the generic ALKYL symbol A)

AOXOA,OA.OA	Ortho-carbonates	S:YA.A	Thioketones
AOYA.OA	Acetals	S:YA.SH	Dithioic acids
ASXA,A.SA	Mercaptols	S:YGA	Thioacyl chlorides
ASYA.SA	Mercaptals	S:YQA	Thionic acids
AXA,A.A	Neoalkanes	S:YZMMA	Thiosemicarbazides *
AYA.A	Isoalkanes	S:YZMN;A	Thiosemicarbazones *
AYA.:NN:YA.A	Ketazines	WNYA.;NQ	Nitrolic acids
M:YA.OA	Imido-esters	ZMYA.:M	Imidrazides
M:YGA	Imide chlorides	ZN:YA.A	Keto-hydrazones
M:YZMA	Guanidines *	ZN;YA.MZ	Hydrazide-hydrazones
QN:YA.A	Ketoximines	ZYA.:M	Amidines
QN:YA.N:O	Nitrosolic acids	ZYA.:NN:YZA	Dihydrazidines
QYA.OA	Hemiacetals	ZYA.;NQ	Amidoximes
QYA.:M	Imidic acids	ZYA.;NZ	Amidrazones
QYA.;NQ	Hydroxamic acids	ZYVQA	*alpha*-Amino acids

* Note that the *longest* sequence of marks (including colons) in these three cases does not start with the highest-ranking terminal sequence. Rule 3 (page 34) determines the citing order of the first and last groups, and the one or two "side groups," at each branching point. Specific alkyl derivatives will have the same citing sequence as shown above if the letter A is replaced by a single digit.

Table 7 illustrates a number of less familiar structure types which contain the "iso"-Y and "neo"-X types of branched carbon atoms.

Structural segments containing two side groups are punctuated with comma and period if the side groups are not strictly terminal monovalent groups; and the period alone suffices for the last or only side group requiring terminating punctuation.

The importance of the punctuation should be evident in these examples:

O		O		O	
QPA	QPOA	QPCN	QPOCN	HSPA	HSPOA
H	H	Q	Q	Q	Q

QPHO.A   QPHOA   QPQO.CN   QPQOCN   SHPQO.A   SHPQOA

ALKYL CHAINS AND POLYMETHYLENE CONNECTIVES

Arabic numerals are reserved to denote the most common of all chain-forming atomic groups — the *n*-alkyl terminals or polymethylene connectives (and their terminally unsaturated derivatives) listed in Table 8. All of these straight-chain hydrocarbon units are defined in terms of the *number of contained carbon atoms*. Thus a single numeral defines the constantly encountered short carbon

Table 8. UNBRANCHED ALKYL GROUP SYMBOLS

1—	Methyl, CH_3—	6:	Hexylidene
1:	Methylene, CH_2:	6::	Hexylidyne
1::	Methylidyne, CH:	7—	Heptyl, n-C_7H_{15}—
2—	Ethyl, CH_3CH_2—	8—	Octyl, n-C_8H_{17}—
—2—	Ethylene, —CH_2CH_2—	9—	Nonyl, n-C_9H_{19}—
2:	Ethylidene, CH_3CH:	1ø—	Decyl, n-$C_{10}H_{21}$
2::	Ethylidyne, CH_3C:	11—	*Undecyl*
3—	Propyl, n-C_3H_7	12—	Dodecyl (Lauryl)
—3—	Trimethylene	14—	Tetradecyl
3:	Propylidene, C_3H_6:	16—	*Hexadecyl* (Cetyl)
3::	Propylidyne, C_3H_5:	18—	Octadecyl
4—	Butyl, n-C_4H_9—	2ø—	Eicosyl
—4—	Tetramethylene	26—	Hexacosyl
4:	Butylidene, C_4H_8:	3ø—	Triacontyl
4::	Butylidyne	4ø—	Tetracontyl
5—	*Pentyl* (*n*-Amyl)	5ø—	Pentacontyl
—5—	Pentamethylene	6ø—	Hexacontyl
5:	*Pentylidene*	A—	Alkyl (any)
5::	*Pentylidyne*	—A—	Polymethylene
6—	Hexyl, n-C_6H_{13}—	A:	Alkylidene
—6—	Hexamethylene	A::	Alkylidyne

Note how the zero is "slashed" to avoid confusion with the letter O. The above names are taken from the IUPAC Report (see second footnote in Table 1); new recommendations or preferences are italicized.

chain with an ultimate of simplicity and brevity. These linear carbon atoms are fully hydrogenated within the enumerated chain; unsaturations are shown with interposed colons, which denote linkage of smaller fundamental chains. The zero numeral always is slashed as Ø to avoid ambiguity with the letter O (for oxygen), and in text copy the alkane numerals are distinguished with a suffixed letter H (for hydrocarbon). Thus methane, ethane, and decane can be denoted here as 1H, 2H, and 1ØH.

Linear combinations of these aliphatic symbols lucidly reflect the symmetry of the structure. Thus 1:1 is ethylene; 1:2:1, butadiene; 2M2, diethylamine; 3O3, dipropyl ether; 4SS4, dibutyl disulfide; 5OVO5, pentyl carbonate; E1E, methylene bromide; G2S2G, mustard gas; O:2:O, glyoxal; Q2O2Q, diglycol; Q2Q, glycol; QV2VQ, succinic acid; Z2Z, ethylene diamine; and ZV4VZ, adipamide.

REVIEW EXERCISES

1. Translate to structure diagrams with valence lines and familiar atomic symbols:

GOG	Chlorine monoxide	WNONW	Nitric anhydride
IG	Iodine monochloride	WSGG	Sulfuryl chloride
NCG	Cyanogen chloride	WSO	Sulfur trioxide
OE *	Bromine peroxyl	ZG	Chloramine
OPGGG	Phosphoryl chloride	ZN:M	Triazene
QQ	Hydrogen peroxide	ZNW	Nitramide
WGO.OGWO	Chorine heptoxide	ZQ	Hydroxylamine
WNG	Nitryl chloride	ZZ	Hydrazine

2. Name the following inorganic acids:

EH	QN:NQ	QPQPQQ	WNOQ	WSQOQ
GH	QN:O	QSO.SQO	WNQ	WSQQ
NN:M	QPHHO	SSQQO	WSQG	WSQSWQ
QBHQ	QPHQO	WGQO	WSQNO.:NQ	ZMSWQ
QBQQ	QPQQO	WIQ	WSQON:O	ZSWQ
QG				

3. Show the difference between the following sets of isomers with conventional valence-line diagrams (show single coordinate links with arrows):

GSOG vs. OSGG   WNNW vs. WNON:O

QN:O vs. WNH   WNF   vs. O:NOF

ZVZ   vs. ZM1:O and ZHH,.OCN   QSQ   vs. QSHO
QCN   vs. OCM and QNC   QSQO   vs. WSHQ
WSQON:O vs. WSQNW, WNOSQO, QOSWN:O, or WNSO.OQ

4. Describe the following carbonyl derivatives with systematic
   symbols:

Biuret, $NH_2CO.NHCO.NH_2$ Formamide, NH_2CHO
Carbamic acid, $NH_2CO.OH$ N-Nitrocarbamic acid,
Carbazide, $(NH_2NH)_2CO$ O_2N—$NHCO.OH$
Carbonic acid, H_2CO_3 Nitrourea, $NH_2CO.NHNO_2$
Carbonyl azide, $(N_3)_2CO$ Peroxycarbonic acid, H_2CO_4
Carbonyl fluobromide,   Phosgene, $COCl_2$
   COFBr   Semicarbazide, $NH_2CO.NHNH_2$
Chloroformic acid, $ClCO.OH$ Urea, $(NH_2)_2CO$
Formaldehyde, H_2CO Urethane, $NH_2CO.OC_2H_5$

5. Arrange the above carbonyl structure descriptions in alphabetic
   order.
6. Which of the above carbonyl derivatives have primary amino or
   NH_2 groups?

Answers:

2. Hydrobromic acid, hydrochloric acid, hydrazoic acid, borous acid, boric acid,
   hypochlorous acid, hyponitrous acid, nitrous acid, hypophosphorous acid,
   phosphorous acid, phosphoric acid, hypophosphoric acid, hyposulfurous acid,
   thiosulfuric acid, perchloric acid, meta-iodic acid, peroxynitric acid, nitric
   acid, chlorosulfonic acid, dinitrososulfurous acid, nitrosylsulfuric acid, peroxy-
   monosulfuric acid, sulfuric acid, dithionic acid, hydrazinosulfuric acid, sulfamic
   acid.
4. ZVMVZ, ZVQ, ZMVMZ, QVQ, NNNVNNN, FVE, QVG, O:1, Z1:O,
   WNMVQ, ZVMNW, QVOQ, GVG, ZVMZ, ZVZ, and ZVO2.
6. Z1:O, ZMVMZ, ZVMNW, ZVMVZ, ZVMZ, ZVO2, ZVQ, and ZVZ.

3

AUXILIARY SYMBOLS

PUNCTUATION MARKS

The various *modes of connection* (or branched disconnection) of the atomic group symbols are denoted in a logical and familiar manner with punctuation marks — such as the colon for an ethylenic unsaturation, and the period or comma for side-group terminations (as illustrated in Tables 3, 6, and 7).

The *colon* (or semicolon) always is used to denote unsaturations associated with the alkyl-chain numerals and with the letter Y (a Y-forked :C— atom). The colon is modified with a *comma* to denote a *cis* linkage, and with a *sTroke* to denote a *trans* linkage. The geometric shape always is determined by the longest line of symbols (or the main chain), C-shaped being *cis* and S-shaped being *trans*.

Thus

$$
2\text{:,}2 \text{ denotes} \quad
\begin{matrix} \text{CH—CH}_3 \\ \| \\ \text{CH—CH}_3 \end{matrix}
\quad \text{and} \quad 2\text{:/}2 \text{ denotes} \quad
\begin{matrix} \text{CH—CH}_3 \\ \| \\ \text{CH}_3\text{—CH} \end{matrix}
$$

(It should be clear that *pairs* of punctuation marks can be used without ambiguity just as readily as pairs of letters, such as Ac and Ca or Ba and Ra.) Colons are counted as graphical symbols, but the modifying marks — like stereoisomeric marks — are not. The *semicolon* is used in place of the colon to identify potential but unresolved *cis-trans* unsaturations, such as 2;2 for 2-butene. Other examples are given in Tables 9–12.

Acetylenic linkages (triple bonds) also can be shown easily with a

Table 9. COMPOUND RADICALS CONTAINING ALKYL
CHAINS AND OXYGEN GROUPS

1O—	Methoxy	7V—	*Octanoyl*
1OV—	*Methoxycarbonyl*	8V—	*Nonanoyl*
1OVV—	Methoxalyl	9:,8V—	Oleoyl
1:1O—	Vinyloxy	9V—	*Decanoyl*
1:1V—	Acryloyl	1ØV—	*Undecanoyl*
1:2O—	*Allyloxy*	11V—	Lauroyl
1::CV—	Propioloyl	12V—	Tridecanoyl
1V—	Acetyl	13V—	Myristoyl
1V1—	Acetonyl	14V—	*Pentadecanoyl*
1V1:	Acetonylidene	15V—	Palmitoyl
1V1V—	*Acetoacetyl*	16V—	Heptadecanoyl
1VO—	Acet*yl*oxy	17V—	Stearoyl
1VV—	Pyruvoyl	AO—	[Alkyloxy]
2O—	Ethoxy	—O1O—	Methylenedioxy
2OV—	*Ethoxycarbonyl*	O:1—	Formyl
2OVV—	Ethoxalyl	O:1O—	*Formyloxy*
2:/1V—	Crotonoyl	O:1V—	Glyoxyloyl
2V—	Propionoyl	Q1—	[Hydroxymethyl]
2VO—	*Propionoyloxy*	Q1V—	Glycoloyl
3O—	Propoxy	Q2—	[Hydroxyethyl]
3;3;3;8V—	[Linolenoyl] *	—V1:,1V—	*Maleoyl*
3V—	Butyroyl	—V1:/1V—	*Fumaroyl*
3VO—	[Butyroyloxy]	—V1V—	Malonoyl
4O—	Butoxy	—V2V—	Succinoyl
4V—	Valeroyl	—V3V—	Glutaroyl
5O—	Pentyloxy	—V4V—	Adipoyl
5V—	Caproyl	—V5V—	*Pimeloyl*
6O—	*Hexyloxy*	—V6V—	*Suberoyl*
6;3;8V—	[Linoleoyl] *	—V7V—	*Azelaoyl*
6V—	*Heptanoyl*	—V8V—	*Sebacoyl*

* The semicolon denotes an unresolved, potentially *cis-trans* unsaturation.
The above unbracketed names are taken from the IUPAC Nomenclature Report
(see second footnote in Table 1); new recommendations or preferences are
italicized.

pair of colons; such a linkage is in reality a *double* dehydrogenation,
and in molecular orbital theory a *double* unsaturation. Thus 1::1

denotes acetylene, and QVC::2 denotes tetrolic acid

$$(OH—CO.C:C—CH_3)$$

The letter C, however, is preferred to denote unbranched and
isolated C-atom segments, such as those in the ::C—, —CC—, CN—,
CNO—, NC—, NCO—, NCS—, OCN—, and SCN— groups. Thus
allene is denoted 1:C:1 (not 1:1:1), difluoroacetylene is FCCF (not
F1::1F), cyanogen is NCCN (not N::2::N), carbon monoxide is OC

Table 10. COMPOUND RADICALS DENOTED WITH
ALKYL–CHAIN SYMBOLS

1:1—	*Vinyl*	2;2—	2-*Butenyl*
—1;1—	*Vinylene*	—2;2—	2-*Butenylene*
1:2—	*Allyl*	2;2:	2-*Butenylidene*
—1;2—	Propenylene-(1)	2;2::	2-*Butenylidyne*
1:2:	*Allylidene*	2:C:	Propenylidene
1:2;1—	Butadienyl-(1,3)	2::C—	1-Propynyl
1:2::	2-*Butenylidyne*	3;1—	1-Butenyl
1:3—	3-Butenyl	3;2—	2-*Pentenyl*
1:C:	*Vinylidene*	A;A—	[Alkenyl]
1::2—	2-*Propynyl*	A;A;A—	[Alkadienyl]
1::C—	Ethynyl	A::A—	[Alkynyl]
2;1—	1-Propenyl	A::C—	[Acetylenyl]

The unbracketed names in this table and in Table 11 are taken from the IUPAC Nomenclature Report (see first footnote in Table 1, page 7); new recommendations or preferences are italicized.

Table 11. NITROGENOUS AND MISCELLANEOUS
COMBINATIONS WITH ALKYL CHAINS

1VM—	Acetamido	Z1V—	Glycyl
1VN:	Acet*y*limino	ZV2V—	Succinamoyl
2M—	*Ethylamino*	1S—	*Methylthio*
2VM—	*Propionamido*	2AsH—	[Ethylarsino]
6VM—	*Heptanamido*	2S—	*Ethylthio*
AVM—	[Acylamido]	G1—	[Chloromethyl]
—N;1—	[Azomethine]	S:1—	*Thioformyl*
O:1M—	Formamido		

(not O::1), carbon dioxide is OCO (not O:1:O), and ketene is O:C:1 (not O:1:1). The NC group always is shown with these instantly recognizable symbols, as in NCH for hydrogen cyanide, QCN for HOCN, and QNC for HONC. Table 8 (page 17) shows that the hydrocarbon chains are not "broken" to show terminating —C:: atoms, except in the case of this important —CN functional group (which hydrolyzes to —VQ).

The *period* is used in a long-familiar (since 1862) manner to denote termination of a single side group. Thus hexanol-3 is denoted QY3.2 (note that the QY group characterizes secondary alcohols). The *comma* is used at doubly branched points to punctuate the first of two side branches, and the period "terminates" this segment containing two side groups. Thus butylethylpropyl carbinol is denoted QX4,3.2 (note that the QX group characterizes tertiary alcohols).

Table 12. MISCELLANEOUS BRANCHED RADICALS CONTAINING ALKYL GROUPS

1As1.—	Cacodyl
1N1.—	Dimethylamino
1S2YZV—	Methionyl *
2K2,2.—	Triethylammonium
2:1Y4.—	1-Butyl-2-butenyl *
M:YZM3YZV—	Arginyl *
Q1YQV—	Glyceroyl *
Q1YZV—	Seryl *
QV1YZV—	Aspartyl *
QV2YZV—	Glutamyl *
SH1YZV—	Cysteinyl *
—SW1SW—	(Methylenedisulfonyl)
—V1YV—.1V—	Propanetricarbonyl
—V2YZV—	Glutamoyl-(5)
—VYQ1V—	Maloyl
—VYZ1SS1YZV—	Cystyl (—VYZ1S²)
—VYZ1V—	Aspartoyl
—VYZ2V—	Glutamoyl-(1)
WS1.—	Methylsulfonyl
—Y1:1.—	Allylidene
—Y1:2.—	2-Butenylidene
—Y2.—	Propylidene
—Y3.—	Butylidene
—Y4.—	*Pentyl*idene
—Y5.—	Hexylidene
—Y:.—	Vinylidene
Z2SW—	Tauryl
Z3YZV—	Ornithyl *
Z4YZV—	Lysyl *
ZV1YZV—	Asparaginyl *
ZV2YZV—	Glutaminyl *
ZY4.V—	Norleucyl

* In these cases, note that the *longest* sequence of marks (letters, colons, and numerals) does not begin with the highest-ranking terminal sequence.

Note the numero-alphabetic order of rank (Rule 2a, page 33), the "longest symbol sequence" orientation (Rule 3a, page 34), and subordination of the H-symbol (Rule 6a, page 45).

Stereoisomeric distinctions are indicated by the use of a *comma* for the D- (dee) or "dropped" orientation, and a *stroke* for the L- (ell) or "lifted" orientation. Thus D-glycerose (D-glyceraldehyde) is diagrammatically described as shown in the $\quad$ Q1Y1:O inset, and delineated as Q1YQ,1:O. The corresponding $\quad$ Q L-stereoisomer is delineated Q1YQ/1:O. The main-line orientation is defined more precisely in Rule 5b, page 44 (the more intricately related *dextro-* or *levo-rotary* nature is indicated with a suffixed italic letter, as Q1YQ,1:O-*d*).

Cation-anion halves of ionic salts are distinguished by a separating set of *comma-period* marks, "polarized" with the comma on the cationic side. Thus the quaternary tetraethylammonium chloride [Et₄N][Cl] is denoted 2K2,2.2,.G and calcium oxalate is denoted OVVO.,Ca.

The *hyphen* denotes a free valence terminal (shown by a long line in the tables). It is used in a similar manner to distinguish an intercyclic linkage, described in Rule 25a, page 88. *Pairs of hyphens* are used to set off the repeating units in polymers, in order to distinguish this "head-to-tail" type of repetition from centrosymmetric forms. Thus hexaethylene glycol is denoted Q-2O-⁵2Q, with a superscript multiplier used as defined in Rule 10c, page 56. Pairs of hyphens are used in an analogous manner to set off any two-letter atomic symbols that follow a ring symbol; thus possible ambiguities with the lower-case positional letters (Rule 12, page 65) are avoided.

The *asterisk* is reserved as a suffix mark to denote activated (energy-rich) centers in molecules, such as 20V1*VO2 for the —CH₂— activated malonic ester.

The *sharp mark* ♯ is used as a conspicuous generic suffix to "tag" labelled atomic groups, such as QV♯2 for "carbonyl-labelled" propionic acid. Alkyl chains may be "broken" by this labelling, as in the alternately labelled QV1♯1 (second or *alpha* carbon atom). *Superscripts* are added to specify the mass number, as in QV♯¹³2 if carbonyl-labelled with C¹³; and the isotopic mixtures may be defined more fully by the use of a suffixed and parenthetically expanded definition of the sharp mark. Thus the complete designation QV♯2 ♯(C¹³,C¹⁴) means that the labelled components consist of a mixture of C¹³ and C¹⁴ atoms.

SUPERSCRIPTS AND SUBSCRIPTS

Ionic charges are indicated in the customary manner with a superscript that always includes the unit numeral and the appropriate algebraic sign, although the latter can be written as ^{m} for minus and ^{p} for plus if the algebraic signs are not available. Thus the fluoroacetate ion is denoted OV1F⁻¹ (or OV1Fᵐ¹). *Free radicals* (molecules containing an odd total number of electrons) are punctuated with a related zero superscript or degree mark. Thus chlorine dioxide, nitric oxide, and nitrogen dioxide may be distinguished as OGO⁰, ON⁰, and ONO⁰.

Superscripts are seldom used in large lists of chemical-structure descriptions because they denote relatively rare or unusual details, such as the isotopic atomic mass numbers or the electronic charges on ions. Since superscripts are required for these purposes, however, they also are profitably employed in the present notation as *multipliers of a sequence of symbols* (like subscripts suffixed to a bracketed expression). Details are given in Rule 10, page 54.

Subscripts are used in a familiar manner in this notation, as detailed in Rule 4d, page 43.

OTHER SYMBOLS

The benzene ring, an extremely common structural component, statistically outnumbers all other rings combined. This extraordinary prominence therefore dictates the "least effort" use of a special letter R to denote this commonest *ring*, a resonating regular hexagon. Thus RR is biphenyl; RVR, benzophenone; RVOR, phenyl benzoate; WNR, nitrobenzene; and ZR, aniline.

Lower-case letters, through their alphabetical order, serve to locate ring positions (Rule 12, page 65). Thus *para*-dichlorobenzene is GRdG and *meta*-dinitrobenzene is WNRcNW. The corresponding phenylene radicals are denoted simply as —Rd— and —Rc—.

Arabic numerals, appropriately "enclosed" within parentheses and punctuated with a saturation character mark, also are used to denote the ring sizes of the corresponding cycloalkanes, such as (5/) for cyclopentane and (66) for naphthalene. Prime marks (or superscripts) are cited between these ring numbers in a pictorially suggestive manner to denote the size of any atomic bridges between nonaromatic rings. Thus the 5,5-ring system in camphor is denoted (5'5) and an alicyclic 6,6-ring system with a two-atom bridge is denoted (6"6). The letter symbols that are used to describe heteratomic or cyclic keto segments within the ring system always are suggestively enclosed within the ring parentheses, as are the fixed unsaturation symbols (locant and colon pairs). Thus (3/M) denotes ethyleneimine (—NH—CH₂CH₂—) and (5/M c:) denotes 3-pyrroline (—NH—CH₂CH:CH—CH₂—).

Aromatic character is suggested with a period instead of a stroke between the ring numeral and the heteratomic symbols; as in (6.N) for pyridine and (5.S) for thiophene. Cyclic branch symbols always are *suffixed* to the "bracketed" ring system description, as in (6.N)cVQ for pyridine-3-carboxylic acid (niacin).

The determination of unique positional relations in polycyclic systems is such a complex problem — it belongs in the mathematical province of *topology* rather than chemistry — that this advanced discussion is deferred until Chapter 8, page 78.

SUMMARY OUTLINE OF SPECIFIC LETTER SYMBOLS *

A. Symbols representing single atoms
  1. One-letter symbols
      (a) Nine international atomic symbols: B, C, F, H, I, N, O, P, S (C, N, and O are restricted to denote H-free structural units)
      (b) Five new assignments:
      E   for bromine
      G   for chlorine

      K   for cationic and fully alkylated $\overset{|}{\underset{|}{N}}{}^{+}$

      X   for quaternary (4-coordinate) aliphatic $\overset{\diagdown}{\underset{\diagup}{C}}{}^{\diagup}_{\diagdown}$

      Y   for singly-forked (3-coordinate) non-carbonyl aliphatic $\overset{\diagdown}{C}{}^{\diagup}$

      (also used for the corresponding saturated

$$\overset{\|}{\underset{|}{—CH—}} \text{ unit)}$$

  2. Two-letter symbols
      (a) Eighty-one international atomic symbols: Ac, *Ag*, AL, Am, As, At, *Au*, Ba, Be, Bi, Bk, Ca, Cd, Ce, Cf, Cm, Co, Cr, Cs, Cu, Dy, Er, Eu, *Fe*, Fr, Ga, Gd, Ge, He, Hf, *Hg*, Ho, In, Ir, Kr, La, Li, Lu, Mg, Mn, Mo, *Na*, Nb, Nd, Ne, Ni, Np, Os, Pa, *Pb*, Pd, Pm, Po, Pr, Pt, Pu, Ra, Rb, Re, Rh, Rn, Ru, *Sb*, Sc, Se, Si, Sm, *Sn*, Sr, Ta, Tb, Tc, Te, Th, Ti, TL, Tm, Xe, Yb, Zn, Zr (those from Latin names are italicized)
      (b) Six new assignments (extensions of present symbols): Ar for argon, Ka for potassium, Ur for uranium, Vd for vanadium, Wf for tungsten (wolfram), and Yt for yttrium

* Suggested by Dr. K. S. Warren of Oak Ridge, Tenn.

B. Letter symbols representing more than one atom (six new one-letter symbols)
  1. Benzene derivatives: R for the benzene ring
  2. Oxygen functions: Q for OH, V for *keto* CO, W for nonlinear "dioxo" O_2
  3. Nitrogen functions: M for NH, Z for NH_2

REVIEW EXERCISES

Nearly all of the examples selected for these exercises describe widely known chemicals — basic raw materials or intermediates, and common health or fire hazards (see Chapter 5 and later chapters for aromatic examples).

1. Decode and identify by chemical name or synonym the following aliphatic hydrocarbons and oxygen derivatives:

(a)	(b)	(c)	(d)	(e)	(f)	(g)	(h)	(i)
1H	OC	1V1	3;2	1::1	5OV1	1OVO1	O:1O4	1VO2O1
2H	Q1	1:1	3V1	1VO1	Q1:O	1:2:1	O:2;2	2O2O2OV1
3H	Q2	2O2	4:1	2OV1	Q2:1	1VOV1	O:C:1	2O2OV1
4H	Q3	2:1	4V1	2VO2	Q2O1	2O2O2	Q2O2Q	Q1YQ1Q
5H	Q4	2;2	O:1	3OV1	Q2O2	2OVO2	QV4VQ	Q2O2O2
6H	Q5	2V1	Q2Q	4OV1	Q2O4	3OVO3	QV8;9	Q2O2O2Q
8H	Q8	3:1	QV1	4OV2	QVVQ	4OVO4	QY2.2	QV8;3;6
			QVQ			O:1O2		QV8;3;3;3

2. Which of the above are: (a) acids, (b) alcohols, (c) aldehydes, (d) esters, (e) ethers, (f) hydrocarbons, (g) ketones, (h) mixed or other functions?
3. Decode and identify the following nitrogen compounds:

(a)	(b)	(c)	(d)	(e)	(f)
NN	1M1	ONN	NCCN	1N1.1	Q2N2Q2Q
ON	2M2	ONO	NN:1	2N2.2	WNO2ONW
Z1	4M4	WN1	ONO2	4N4.4	ZHH,.O3N
Z2	5M5	WN2	WNNW	5N5.5	
Z4	M:3	WN3	WNO2	NC1:1	
Z5	NC1	WNQ		ONONO	
ZH	NC2	ZV1		WNONW	
ZQ	NCH	ZVZ		Z2M2Z	
ZZ		Z2Z			

4. Which of the above are: (a) primary amines, (b) secondary amines, (c) tertiary amines, (d) nitriles, (e) nitroalkanes, (f) nitric esters (g) other types?

5. Identify the following acyclic sulfur compounds:

(a)	(b)	(c)	(d)	(e)
GSG	SCS	GSSG	1OSWO1	1:2S2:1
OSO	SH2	WSQG	G2S2G	SCN2:1
SCO	SHH	WSQQ	WSQO2	WSQONO

6. Identify the following aliphatic halogen-containing compounds:

(a)	(b)	(c)	(d)	(e)	(f)	(g)
E1	E2E	G1:1	G1:1G	G1YG1G	G1YQ1G	GXGGYQO2
E2	G1G	G2:1	G2O2G	G2N1.1	GYG:1G	GYG:YGG
G1	G2F	GYFF	GXGFF	G2N2.2	GYGYGG	O:1XGGG
G5	GVG	GYGF	GXGGG	QVXGGG	WNXGGG	QYQXGGG
I1	NCG	GYGG	GYG1G			
	Q2G	QV1G	QVYGG			

7. Which of the compounds listed in Questions 1–6 are: (a) primary carbon derivatives, (b) "secondary" derivatives, or (c) "tertiary" derivatives? *

8. Identify the following inorganic compounds:

(a)	(b)	(c)	(d)	(e)	(f)	(g)
Ar	GH	G₅P	GPGG	AsHHH	Ka,.I	Ba,.Q₂
EE	IG	OCO	PHHH	GAsGG	Li,.G	CC.,Ca
EH	QG	ONG	QBQQ	GSbGG	Na,.E	O₃G.,Ka
FH	QH	OOO	QPQQ	QPQQO	Na,.Q	Q₂PO₂.,ZHH
GG	QQ	WNF				ZHH,.G

9. Which of the above are: (a) hydrides, (b) covalent compounds, (c) ionic salts?

---

* See note on definitions at the end of Chapter 2.

Part Two

ALIPHATIC (OPEN-CHAIN) COMPOUNDS

4

THE LINE–FORMULA CONVENTION

Simplicity of usage means the employment of just a few natural and widely applicable basic principles; it thus means a careful harmony of all the conventions now in use. One of the most widely established conventions in notational expressions relates to the linear structure descriptions that appear in virtually every chemical handbook, dictionary, catalog, or price list throughout the world. The exact convention relating to "linear expression of formulae" was clearly defined by Dr. A. D. Mitchell*: "Each full point is regarded as separating two atoms which are directly linked in the main chain of a compound, and atoms or groups attached to each of these atoms are written immediately *after* it and before the next full point." His inorganic examples are $NH_2 \cdot SO_2 \cdot OH$, $PH_2O \cdot OH$, $PH(OH)_2$, and $PO(OH)_2 \cdot O \cdot PO(OH)_2$. Dr. Mitchell reminds the reader that, "hydrogen takes precedence of other atoms, coming immediately after the relevant atom in the main chain," not, "as is often done," *before* the first atom in the main chain.

This line-formula convention is observed in the structure explanations given hereafter in this manual, with a further refinement that was suggested by the "new notations" of H. Wichelhaus, published in 1867: *periods* are used only to set off "side group" discontinuities other than H atoms (such as the O-atom symbol in carbonyl groups), and *hyphens* are used to set off the directly connected atoms and hydrogenated groups (such as the alkyl-chain and —NH— segments).

The line-formula delineations that first appeared in 1861 (see

* A. D. Mitchell, "British Chemical Nomenclature," E. Arnold & Co., London, 1948, p. 2.

Appendix A) soon proved to be almost as lucid as the graphical diagrams, yet they greatly conserved journal space and writing time. The basic effort-saving aim is emphasized as the first and most important rule of this new notation.

1. "LEAST EFFORT" DELINEATION

RULE 1a Cite all chains of structural units symbol by symbol as connected.

Thus *

$$CH_3CH_2CH_2CH_2CH_2—O—CO.NH—CO.O—CH_2CH_2CH_2CH_2CH_3$$
is denoted 5OVMVO5
$$OH—CH_2CH_2—S—CH_2CH_2CH_2CH_2CH_2CH_2—S—CH_2CH_2—OH$$
is Q2S6S2Q
$$NH_2—CO.CH_2CH_2CH_2CH_2—CO.NH_2$$ is ZV4VZ

Note that the symmetry of the structure is reflected in the symbolism.

RULE 1b Select the shortest necessary structure descriptions as the preferred ones. Thus the colon never is used to show unsaturations that "resonate" within functional groups such as CN—, NC—, CNO—, NCO—, OCN—, and NNN—. (The colon also may be omitted when groups such as OAs—, OB—, OC:, ON—, and OP— *initiate* the notation.)

2. INDEXING EMPHASIS ON TERMINAL FUNCTIONS

The traditional aim in chemical classification and indexing has been to bring together compounds of similar *function* (as Auguste Laurent defined the term in 1853), such as acids, alcohols, aldehydes, and primary amines. This general organizing aim is common not only in organic textbooks and in physico-chemical considerations, such as toxicity, but also in well-written commercial catalogs, for example, "Synthetic Organic Chemicals" (Carbide & Carbon Chemicals Co., 1952). Again, a traditional aim in subject indexing has been to "invert" compound names in order to *put the most important term first*. Both of these aims are harmonized with the "least effort" delineation through a second notation-orienting rule.

* All of the examples given hereafter to illustrate the rules have been taken from the randomly selected test list used by the ACS Volunteers in the NRC–IUPAC Notation Testing Program.

RULE 2a Resolve all otherwise equal alternatives in symbol sequences by selecting the sequence that gives the *highest* numeroalphabetic listing:

Z Y X W V U T S Ru-Ra* Q P O N M L K J I H G F E D C B A & 9 8 7 6 5 4 3 2 1
(Highest first)   (Lowest last)

This row of symbols represents the full range of marks available (and the sequence automatically obtained) with standard tabulating equipment. Therefore punctuation marks are alphabetized (and denoted on tabulating keyboards) by making a *colon* or semicolon equivalent to the letter U (unsaturation), a *stroke* to T (tilted mark), a *hyphen* to L (line), and the *comma* or *period* ("separators") to the indicated ampersand or thirty-seventh character. *Lower-case letters* are distinguished simply by making them equivalent to capital letters *prefixed by a blank space*. This "empty column" automatically gives these locant marks lower rank than the numerals. Superscripts and subscripts likewise are distinguished by a prefixed blank space, and thus have the lowest rank of all. Examples of the "highest first" orientation, taken from the test list, are:

NH_2—CH_2CH_2—CO.NH—CH_2—CO.NH—CH_2—CO.OH
                 is Z2VM1VM1VQ (Z before Q)
Cl—CH_2CH_2—NH—CO.O—CH_2CH_3
                 is G2MVO2   (G before 2)
CH_3CH_2—S—CO.NH—CH_2CH_3
                 is 2SVM2   (2S- before 2M-)
CH_3—CO.CH_2CH_2—CO.O—CH_2CH:CH_2
                 is 1V2VO2:1   (1V- before 1:-)
CH_2:CH—CO.O—CH_2CH_2—O—CH_2CH_2—O—CH_3
                 is 1:1VO2O2O1   (1:- before 1O-)

Similarly, SCN— would rank before SeH— because the latter sorts as S EH—.

RULE 2b Indicate *ethylenic unsaturations* by the colon (or semicolon) when these are associated with alkylene groups (aldo, etc.), with Y-bonded —C: atoms, or with potentially *cis-trans*
                             |
linkages (azo, *syn*, *anti*, etc.).
Thus:

CH_3CH:$CHCH_2$—O—CO.CH:CH_3 is 2:2OV1:1   (or 2;2OV1:1)
NC—CH_2—N:CH_2 is NC1N:1
NH_2—CO.NH—N:CHCH:$CHCH_3$ is ZVMN:2:2 (or ZVMN;2;2)

* See Rule 11 for the special rank of the benzene ring symbol R.

RULE 2c   Indicate *acetylenic unsaturations* with a double colon, when cited as required by Rule 1b (not within NC— groups nor —CC— connectives).

Thus CH_3—$CO.C\colon CCH_2$—O—CH_3 is   1VC::2O1

The carbon chain in the $\equiv CCH_2$— connective, like the corresponding alkylidyne terminal, is not broken into separately symbolized parts (see Table 8, page 17).

3. NOTATIONAL CLARITY IN BRANCHED STRUCTURES

Graphical diagrams of many open-chain structures are complicated by the fact that each branch adds an additional terminal symbol — a potential starting point.   Hence the *easiest* and *most recognizable* delineation of highly branched structures will not always be determined by Rule 2 alone, particularly when the highest-ranking terminal letter represents a side group near the middle of an intricately branched chain.   Nor will Rule 2a give the most favorable numero-alphabetic distribution for *ease of manipulation by machine methods*, because the Z and Q divisions will tend to be overloaded, and the lower-ranking letter and number divisions will tend to be underloaded.   Therefore the third rule is designed to improve both the notational clarity and the indexing efficiency of aliphatic and benzenoid structure descriptions.

RULE 3a   Cite all *singly* forked structures through the longest line of graphical symbols, denoting the side group *after* the symbol to which it is attached.

This rule rigorously defines "side groups" as those atoms or branches denoted by the fewest graphical symbols — letters, colons (or semicolons), and numerals.*

RULE 3b   Omit the punctuation for side groups ending with the strictly terminal symbols —E, —F, —G, —H, —Q, —W, and —Z.   (Stereoisomeric punctuations are given in Rule 5b.)   Examples with symmetric main chains are delineated in a familiar manner; lucid diagrams "unfold" the parts:

---

* The branch-delineating procedure reduces to a simple, purely mechanical count of the graphical symbols when colons (or semicolons) are counted with other symbols.   Furthermore, the thiocarbonyl (S:Y—) or imido (M:Y—) groups then are characterized by the initial symbols S: and M:, which seldom appear first in listings.

W
CH_3—O—SO_2—O—CH_3 is denoted   1OSWO1 *   1OSO1
CH_3CH_2—O—CO.CHCl.CO.O—CH_2CH_3
                    is 2OVYGVO2 *   2OVYVO2
                                                                    G

Asymmetric main lines or chains are oriented as before by Rule 2a. Here again the delineations may be clarified by graphical diagrams made with the same symbols:

Cl—CH_2—CHBr.CH_2—Br
                    is denoted G1YE1E and pictured G1Y1E
                                                                    E

NH:C(NH_2)S—$CH_2CH_2CH_2CH_3$
                    is M:YZS4 *   or M:YS4
                                                                    Z

NC—CH_2CH_2—NH—CH(COOH)CH_2CH_2—S—CH_3
                    is NC2MYVQ2S1 *   or NC2MY2S1
                                                                    V
                                                                    Q

OH—CH_2—CHOH.CH:O   Q
                    is Q1YQ1:O *   or Q1Y1:O

OH—CO.CH_2CH(COOH).NH—CH_2CH_2—CN
                    is QV1YVQM2CN *   or QV1YM2CN
                                                                    V
                                                                    Q

                                                                    2
NH_2—CO.NH—C(:S).S—CH_2CH_3 S
                    is ZVMY:S.S2   or ZVMY:S

Note that the period is preferred to clarify the relation of side groups, such as :S in the last example (or :M, —1:O, and —CN), because these groups do not end with a strictly terminal letter. Structures in which some or all of the branches have the same number of graphi-

---

* Note that the longest sequence does not necessarily begin with the highest-ranking terminal.

cal symbols also are resolved by Rule 2a, as in the last example given above, and in the following two examples:

Cl—CO.CHBr.CH$_2$CH$_2$CH$_2$CH$_2$CH$_2$CH$_3$ E
                                                is denoted GVYE6 and pictured GVY6
O$_2$S(OH)CH$_3$ is WSQ1 or WS1
                                                                                    Q

Note in all cases that *only one* terminal symbol can precede the branched-atom symbol.

RULE 3c   Punctuate the single side group branching off a ternary N, P, S, etc., atom with a period if it does not terminate with one of the symbols listed in 3b.

Thus

CH$_3$CH$_2$CH$_2$CH$_2$—S—CH$_2$CH$_2$—N(CH$_2$CH$_3$)$_2$ is denoted 4S2N2.2
NC—CH(CH$_2$CH$_2$CH$_3$).CO.O—CH$_2$CH$_3$ is NCY3.VO2
OH—CH$_2$CH$_2$—NH—CO.CH$_2$—SO.CH$_2$CH:CH$_2$
                                                      is Q2MV1SO.2:1
CH$_3$—SO$_2$.CH$_2$CH$_2$CH$_2$—NCS   is WS1.3NCS
NH$_2$—CH$_2$CH$_2$CH$_2$—N(CH$_2$CH$_2$CH$_2$CH$_2$CH$_3$)$_2$ is Z3N5.5

RULE 3d   Punctuate the first side groups in *quaternary* or higher branchings with commas if necessary (Rule 3b), reserving the period to punctuate the *last* side group cited in this polybranched segment.

Examples requiring neither comma nor period are given first:
                                                                                    F
F$_3$C—CH$_2$—O—CH$_2$CH$_3$ is denoted FXFF1O2 and pictured FX1O2
                                                                                    F

                                                                                    G
Cl$_3$Si—CH:CH$_2$ is GSiGG1:1   or GSi1:1
                                                                                    G

                                                                                    G
NCS—CCl$_3$ is NCSXGGG   or NCSXG
                                                                                    G

                                                                                    Z
(NH$_2$)$_3$C—SCN   is ZXZZSCN   or ZXSCN
                                                                                    Z

Only the period is required in the following example:

OH—CO.C(NH$_2$)(CH$_2$CH$_2$CH$_3$).CH$_2$—CO.OH

$$\text{is QVXZ3.1VQ} \qquad \text{or QVX1VQ}$$

with superscript 3 above and Z below on the right form.

Both comma and period are required in these examples:

(CH$_3$CH$_2$—O)$_2$P(O).CH$_2$CH$_2$CH$_2$CH$_3$

$$\text{is 2OPO,4.O2} \qquad \text{or 2OPO2}$$

CH$_3$CH$_2$—O—CO.C(O—CH$_2$CH$_3$)$_2$CH$_2$CO.O—CH$_2$CH$_3$

$$\text{is 2OVXO2,O2.1VO2} \qquad \text{or 2OVX1VO2}$$

OH—C(CH$_2$CH$_2$CH$_2$CH$_3$)(CH$_2$CH$_3$).CH$_2$—OH

$$\text{is QX4,2.1Q} \qquad \text{or QX1Q}$$

NH$_2$—CO.NH—CO.CH$_2$—S—P(S).(O—CH$_2$CH$_3$)$_2$

$$\text{is ZVMV1SPS,O2.O2 or ZVMV1SPO2}$$

RULE 3e Include the largest possible number of branched atoms in the main chain; and after this, the largest possible number of systematic graphic symbols.

Clarity becomes the prime consideration when complexly branched structures are met, and Rule 3 in its entirety avoids punctuating complications in these structures.

Thus

CH$_3$–S–CH$_2$CH$_2$–CH(NH$_2$)CO.NH–CH(COOH).CH$_2$CH$_2$–S–CH$_3$

is denoted 1S2YZVMYVQ2S1 and pictured as shown here:

$$\begin{array}{ccc} & \text{Q} & \\ \text{Z} & \text{V} & \\ \end{array}$$

1S2YVMY2S1

BRIEF DEFINITIONS RELATING TO THE LINE–FORMULA CONVENTION

TERMINAL ATOM:
    One-coordinate; attached to only ONE atom other than H.

LINEAL ATOM:
    Two-coordinate; attached to TWO atoms other than H.

TERNARY ATOM:
    Three-coordinate; attached to THREE atoms other than H.

QUATERNARY ATOM:
    Four-coordinate; attached to FOUR atoms other than H.

LINE FORMULA:
    A linear sequence of atomic symbols and connecting marks.

SIDE GROUP:
    An atom or atomic group joined to a branched atom and not regarded as the proper beginning nor ending of the delineation.

Note from these definitions that a "secondary" alcohol or halide is characterized by a *ternary* carbon atom, as in isoalkanes (symbol Y); and a "tertiary" derivative is characterized by a *quaternary* carbon atom, as in neoalkanes (symbol X). However, tertiary *amines* do contain a ternary nitrogen atom (symbol N); and quaternary ammonium compounds or amine oxides likewise contain a quaternary nitrogen atom (symbol K).

CONVENTIONAL LISTING AND SORTING RANK OF THE ATOMIC GROUP SYMBOLS

1— Methyl or CH_3— group

2— Ethyl or CH_3CH_2— group
3— Propyl or $CH_3CH_2CH_2$— group
4— Butyl or $n\text{-}C_4H_9$— group

5— Pentyl or $n\text{-}C_5H_{11}$— group

6— Hexyl or $n\text{-}C_6H_{13}$— group

7— Heptyl or $n\text{-}C_7H_{15}$— group

8— Octyl or $n\text{-}C_8H_{17}$— group
9— Nonyl or $n\text{-}C_9H_{19}$— group
1∅— Decyl or $n\text{-}C_{10}H_{21}$— group

—1— Methylene or —CH_2— connective

—2:   —CH_2CH: connective group
:3:: :$CHCH_2C$: connective group
—4.   *n*-Butyl side group (DL or *sym*)

—5,   D-directed (dropped) pentyl branch

—6/   L-directed (lifted) hexyl branch

7;   Heptylidene terminal (unresolved)

8:,   *cis*-Octylidene terminal
9:/   *trans*-Nonylidene terminal
1∅:: Decylidyne terminal

&.,   (Tabulating equivalent of period or comma)

A   Generic symbol for alkyl group or connective

B   Boron atom

C   Carbon atom, H-free, unbranched, and acyclic (as in —CC—, NC—, or OC:)

D   (Reserved as stereoisomeric alternative; see Appendix B)

E   Bromine atom

F   Fluorine atom

G   Chlorine atom

H   Hydrogen atom

I   Iodine atom

J   Generic symbol for halogen atom

K   Nitrogen atom, cationic and alkylated (quaternary if nonaromatic)

L -   (Letter equivalent of hyphen)

M   *M*id-amino —NH— group or i*M*ino :NH group   (Mt   Metallic atom)

N   Nitrogen atom, H-free in nonionic molecule

O   Oxygen atom, H-free in nonionic molecule

P   Phosphorus atom

Q   Hydroxyl or HO— group   (Qh   Coordinately linked H_2O)

R   Benzene *R*ing *R*esidue, C_6H_x

S   Sulfur atom

T /   (Letter equivalent of *s*troke mark)

U :   (Letter equivalent of *U*nsaturation mark)

V   Keto-carbonyl —CO.— connective group

W   Nonlineal dioxo or O_2 group (as in —NO_2 and —SO_2— groups)

X   Carbon atom, quaternary or X-branched and acyclic

Y   Carbon atom, ternary or Y-branched and acyclic (CH or non-ketonic

$$:\overset{|}{C}-)$$

Z   Amino or "hydra*Z*ino" NH_2— group   (Zh Coordinately linked NH_3)

REVIEW EXERCISES

1. Identify the following common commercial chemicals * with systematic symbols, correctly oriented from left to right:

Acetaldehyde, CH_3CHO

Acetic acid, CH_3COOH

Acetic anhydride, $(CH_3CO)_2O$

Acetone, CH_3COCH_3

Acetylene, C_2H_2

Acrylonitrile, $CH_2{:}CHCN$

Adipic acid, $(—CH_2CH_2COOH)_2$

Allyl alcohol, $CH_2{:}CHCH_2OH$

Ammonia, NH_3

Amyl acetate, $CH_3COO(CH_2)_5H$

Amyl alcohol, $n\text{-}C_5H_{11}OH$

Boric acid, H_3BO_3

Butadiene, $CH_2{:}CHCH{:}CH_2$

Butyl acetate, $CH_3COO(CH_2)_4H$

Butyl alcohol, $CH_3CH_2CH_2CH_2OH$

* Selected from Faith, Keyes, and Clark's "Industrial Chemicals," John Wiley & Sons, Inc., New York, 1950.

Carbon dioxide, CO_2
Carbon disulfide, CS_2
Carbon tetrachloride, CCl_4
Chloral, CCl_3CHO
Chloroform, $CHCl_3$
Crotonaldehyde,
    $CH_2CH{:}CHCHO$
Ether (Ethyl), $C_2H_5OC_2H_5$
Ethyl acetate, $CH_3COOCH_2CH_3$
Ethyl alcohol, CH_3CH_2OH
Ethyl chloride, C_2H_5Cl
Ethylene dichloride,
    $ClCH_2CH_2Cl$
Ethylene glycol, $HOCH_2CH_2OH$
Formaldehyde, $HCHO$
Formic acid, $HCOOH$

Glycerine, $HOCH_2CHOHCH_2OH$
Hydrochloric acid, HCl
Methyl alcohol, CH_3OH
Methyl chloride, CH_3Cl
Methyl ethyl ketone,
    $CH_3COCH_2CH_3$
Nitric acid, HNO_3
Nitropropane, $CH_3CH_2CH_2NO_2$
Oxalic acid, $(COOH)_2$
Phosphoric acid, H_3PO_4
Phosphorus oxychloride, $POCl_3$
Sulfuric acid, H_2SO_4
Trichloroethylene, $ClCH{:}CCl_2$
Urea, NH_2CONH_2
Vinyl acetate, $CH_3COOCH{:}CH_2$
Vinyl chloride, $CH_2{:}CHCl$

2. Draw the graphical diagrams with systematic symbols for the above-described chloral, glycerine, phosphoric acid, phosphorus oxychloride, sulfuric acid, trichloroethylene, and the following:

Chloral hemiacetal, $CCl_3CH(OH)OC_2H_5$
Chloral hydrate, $CCl_3CH(OH)_2$
beta-Chloroethyl diethylamine, $(C_2H_5)_2NCH_2CH_2Cl$
Chloropicrin, CCl_3NO_2
Chlorosulfonic acid, $ClSO_2OH$
sym-Dichlorohydrin, $(ClCH_2)_2CHOH$
Diethylcarbinol, $(CH_3CH_2)_2CHOH$
Diethylcarbinol acetate, $(CH_3CH_2)_2CHOCO.CH_3$
Dimethyl sulfate, $(CH_3)_2SO_4$
Freon-12, CCl_2F_2
Freon-114, $(CClF_2)_2$
Lewisite, $Cl_2AsCH{:}CHCl$
Nitrogen mustard, $CH_3N(CH_2CH_2Cl)_2$
Nitrosylsulfuric acid, $ONOSO_2OH$
Perchloroethylene, $Cl_2C{:}CCl_2$
n-Triamylamine, $(C_5H_{11})_3N$
sym-Trichloropropane, $(ClCH_2)_2CHCl$

3. Delineate the resulting graphical diagrams with the correct left-to-right orientation. How many of these appeared in the exercises for Chapters 2 and 3?

4. Which of the following structure descriptions are incorrectly oriented? Correct them and compare with the lists given in Chapters 2 and 3.

Allyl isothiocyanate	1:2NCS	Freon-21	GYFG
Carbonyl sulfide	OCS	Freon-22	GYFF
Cyanogen chloride	NCG	Hydrogen cyanide	HCN
Diazomethane	NN:1	Hydroxylamine	QZ
Dichloracetic acid	GYGVQ	Monochloracetic acid	G1VQ
Ethyl nitrite	ONO2	Nitrous oxide	NNO
Ethylene chlorohydrin	G2Q	Nitryl fluoride	WNF
Ethylsulfuric acid	QSWO2	Propylidenimine	3:M
Formic acid	O:1Q	Trichloracetic acid	GXGGVQ

5. Can you think of any common chemical names that are more concise than the corresponding systematic line-formula descriptions?

Answers:

1. O:2, QV1, 1VOV1, 1V1, 1::1, NCl:1, QV4VQ, Q2:1, ZH, 5OV1, Q5, QBQQ, 1:2:1, 4OV1, Q4, OCO, SCS, GXGGG, O:1XGGG, GYGG, O:2:2, 2O2, 2OV1, Q2, G2, G2G, Q2Q, O:1, Q1:O, Q1YQ1Q, GH, Q1, G1, 2V1, WNQ, WN3, QVVQ, QPQQO, OPGGG, WSQQ, GYG:1G, ZVZ, 1VO1:1, G1:1.

2.

G		O	G			G	G	G
O:1XG	Q1Y1Q	QPQ	OPG	WSQ	GY:1G	GX—YO2	QY—XG	
G	Q	Q	G	Q	G	G Q	Q G	

	G						F
G2N2	WNXG	WSQ	G1Y1G	QY2	2YOV1	1OSO1	GXG
2	G	G	Q	2	2	W	F

F F						
GX—XG	GAs1:1G	G2N2G	WSONO	GY:YG	5N5	G1Y1G
F F	G	1	Q	G G	5	G

3. (after GYG:1G) GXGGYQO2, QYQXGGG, G2N2.2, WNXGGG, WSQG, G1YQ1G, QY2.2, 2Y2.OV1 *, 2OSWO2, GXGFF, GXFF ²*, GAsG1:1G *, G2N1.2G *, WSQONO, GYG:YGG, 5N5.5, G1YG1G. All but the four marked by asterisk appeared in the earlier list.

4. The correct notations are: SCN2:1, SCO, NCG, NN:1, QVYGG, Q2G, ONO2, WSQO2, Q1:O, GYGF, GYFF, NCH, ZQ, QV1G, WNF, ONN, M:3, and QVXGGG (The colon is not necessary in the *initiating* O:NO2).

5. Complex drugs are among the few examples having short names and long notations.

5

MISCELLANEOUS OPEN–CHAIN DETAILS

The three basic rules given in the preceding chapter suffice for all kinds of branching complications in open-chain molecules. Miscellaneous details relating to ionic salts, geometric isomers, labelled atoms, and special orientations are given in this chapter. The discussion of aliphatic or open-chain structures concludes with the recognition of some important effort-saving contractions specified in Chapter 6.

4. IONIC AND MOLECULAR SALTS

RULE 4a Cite ionic and molecular salts as separate units, first describing the ion or molecule containing the longest symbolism. (Resolve further alternatives by Rules 2 and 3.) Separate the ion pairs by a *comma-period* punctuation, with the comma on the cationic side. Separate any postulated addition compounds (amine hydrohalides, etc.) by a *stroke-period* marking.

Thus

[O—CO.CH₂—CHOH.CH₂—F][Na]	is denoted	OV1YQ1F.,Na
[S—CS.O—CH₂CH₂CH₂CH₃][K]	is	S:YS.O4.,Ka
Hg(CN)₂.HgO	is	NCHgCN/.HgO
[NH₂—C:NH.NH₂][OH—CO.C₁₇H₃₅]	is	ZYZ:M/.QV17
NH₂—CH₂CH₂—NH₂·H₂O	is	Z2Z/.QH

(For a further refinement in postulated "addition" compounds where proton transfer actually takes place, as in the last two examples, the stroke-period marking may be "polarized" like the comma-period marking, with the period on the protonic (acid) side.) The next rule is designed to maintain close correspondence between descriptions of amine bases and those of their salts, by citing the amine base identically in both cases.

RULE 4b Do not change the organic-base orientations to show postulated proton transfers. (Thus a protonic H alternatively may be cited immediately after a Z, S, Q, O, N, M, P, etc., to indicate its transfer, without the addition of coding uncertainties.)

n-$C_{12}H_{25}$—NH—CH_3.HBr   is coded 12M1/.EH
(rather than 12MH1,.E)

[NH_2—CO.SH][NH_2CO.CH_2—NH_2] is ZVSH/.ZV1Z
(rather than ZV1ZH,.ZVS)

RULE 4c Denote tertiary sulfur, quaternary nitrogen, and analogous "onium" compounds as ionic salts, with the period-comma punctuation. Denote *simple* ammonium salts in the same manner, with ZHH for the ammonium ion.

Thus

[(Cl—CH_2CH_2)$_2$N(OH)—CH_2CH_3][Cl]	is denoted	G2KQ2.2G,.G
[(Cl—CH_2CH_2)$_3$S][Cl]	is	G2S2G2G,.G
(O_3S—CH_2CH_2—Cl)(NH_4)	is	WSO.2G.,ZHH
NH_4HCO_3	is	ZHH,.QVO
NH_4SCN	is	ZHH,.SCN

RULE 4d Use subscripts as multipliers of monatomic ions in the usual manner, and as multipliers *higher than two* for oxygen or halogen groups in symmetric anions. (See Rules 10b–10f for superscript extensions)

Thus

[O—CO.CHOH.CH(CO.O).CH_2—CO.O][Na_3]
is denoted OVYQYVO.1VO.,Na_3
O_2As—CH_3.Na_2 is WAs1.,Na_2

Examples of inorganic applications * (not in the NRC–IUPAC Test List) that should be self-explanatory are: ONO.,Na (not

---

* Inorganic chemists not practiced in the use of the "dioxo" W would prefer O_4G to WGW, O_4Os to WOsW, O_4P to WPW, and O_4S to WSW — particularly since these subscripts among strictly inorganic notations could be printed as on-line numerals.

$O_2N.,Na)$, $O_3N.,Ka$, $O_3C.,Ca$, $O_3POPO_3.,Na_4$, $O_4G.,Ka$, $O_4P.,Na_3$, $F_6As.,ZHH$, $F_6Si.,Na_2$, $G_6Pt.,Ka_2$, and $Q_6Pt.,H_2$.

The single-group multiplier also is justified when the subscript *replaces more than three* notational marks (see Rule 10b), as in G_5P, F_6S, F_7I, and F_8Os.

RULE 4e Denote coordinately linked molecules of water and ammonia by using a lower-case h for the hydrogen atom. These Qh (water) and Zh (ammonia) symbols then permit the use of subscript multipliers in structures analogous to those cited above, such as $Qh_6Mg.,O_4S$, $Qh_6Fe.,O_4S/.Qh$, $Zh_3CrQh_3.,G_3$, $Zh_4Cu.,O_3N^2$, $Zh_4CrQQh.,G_2$, and $Zh_5CrQh.,F_6Fe$.

*Multi*solvated molecules of water usually are coordinately bound to a large extent in inorganic salts. Therefore the Qh symbol is justified when the exact coordination is not indicated or not certain, as in $O_4Cr.,Na_2/.Qh_4$, $O_4S.,Zn/.Qh_7$, $O_7B_4.,Li_2/.Qh_5$, $QPO_3.,Na_2/.Qh_{12}$, and $Q_2PO_2.,Na/.Qh_2$.

5. CIS–TRANS UNSATURATIONS AND D–L STEREOISOMERS

RULE 5a Denote the ethylenic *cis* unsaturation (corresponding to a C-shaped main chain) with a colon-*comma* punctuation, and the *trans* (corresponding to an S-shaped main chain) with a colon-*stroke* punctuation.

Thus the

cis-$CH_3(CH_2)_7CH:CH(CH_2)_7CO.NH$—$CH_2CH_3$ is denoted 9:,8VM2

$trans$-OH—$CO.(CH_2)_7CH:CH(CH_2)_8H$ is QV8:/9

The semicolon is reserved, as previously mentioned, to call attention to unresolved (but resolvable) *cis-trans* linkages.

RULE 5b Distinguish stereoisomeric directions by punctuating the D-directed or "dropped" side groups with a comma, and the L-directed or "lifted" ones with a stroke. Orient the main chain to curl backward, away from the observer, in accord with Emil Fischer's original convention (showing the adding aldo end of sugar chains on the *right* side of a *horizontal* line.) *

---

* C. S. Hudson, in "Advances in Carbohydrate Chemistry," Academic Press, Inc., New York, 1948, Vol. III, page 5, gave Fischer's sugar formula as follows: $CH_2(OH) \cdot CH(OH) \cdot CH(OH) \cdot CH(OH) \cdot CH(OH) \cdot COH$ (Fischer, 1891).

Thus D-glycerose (D-glyceraldehyde) is pictured as shown Q1Y1:O
in the inset and delineated as Q1YQ,1:O. All of the   Q
D-series sugars derived from this parent form also begin
with the same Q1YQ, marks. The L-series sugars begin
with the Q1YQ/ marks.

If the Y-branched carbon atom were alkylated to a quaternary
(X-branched) atom by an ethyl group, for example, the stereoisomers
would be Q1XQ,2/1:O and Q1XQ/2,1:O. Racemic or unresolved
side groups may be distinguished with the period punctuation.

RULE 5c Denote consecutive —CH(OH).— segments by citing only
the first YQ letters plus the *full* number of stereoisomeric
marks (comma, stroke, period).*

Thus

$$\begin{array}{ccccccc}
 & & & H & & & 2 \\
H & H & H & \dot{O} & H & H & Q \quad S \\
HO—\dot{C}—\dot{C}—\dot{C}—\dot{C}—\dot{C}—C(S—CH_2CH_3)_2 & or & Q1YYYYYS2 \\
\dot{H} & \dot{O} & \dot{O} & \dot{H} & \dot{O} & & QQ \quad Q \\
 & \dot{H} & \dot{H} & & \dot{H} & &
\end{array}$$

is denoted Q1YQ,,/,YS2.S2

The unspecified

OH—CH$_2$—(CHOH)$_3$CO.CH$_2$—OH   is denoted   Q1YQ...V1Q

RULE 5d Indicate the direction of optical rotation (when specified)
by a suffixed and hyphenated italic letter, -*d* for dextro-
rotary or -*l* for levorotary nature. Thus D-glyceraldehyde
may be elaborated as Q1YQ,1:O-*d*.

6. SPECIAL ORIENTATIONS

RULE 6a Cite the H-atom symbol directly after the symbol to which
it is attached.

Thus

(CH$_3$CH$_2$CH$_2$CH$_2$CH$_2$CH$_2$CH$_2$—O)$_2$PHO   is denoted 7OPHO.O7
SH—CH$_2$CH(NH$_2$)CO.NH—CH$_2$—CO.O—CH$_3$
is SH1YZVM1VO1

Note that this rule rigidly follows the classical line-formula convention, in the relatively infrequent cases where the letter H must be
used.

* A more advanced application, discussed in Appendix B, employs the symbol D for a "dropped" group and L for a "lifted" one.

RULE 6b   Denote amino acid NH_2—$CH(COOH)$— terminals with a specially oriented ZYVQ— notation, becoming ZYVQ,— for the "dropped" orientation in the D_s (dee-serine) series and ZYVQ/— for the "lifted" orientation in the L_s (ell-serine) series.   (Compare with designations in Rule 5b)

Thus   L-serine
$$COOH$$
$$|$$
$$NH_2—CH—CH_2—OH$$
is delineated   ZYVQ/1Q

and the D_s-form of NH_2—$CH(COOH)CH_2CH_2$—$SO.CH_3$

is   ZYVQ,2SO.1

The high-ranking ZYVQ letter sequence brings these important acids together in alphabetic listings; and *the stereo-sign remains unchanged* when the corresponding terminal groups are delineated as suffixes to a ring system symbolism.   That is, ZYVQ/— is the same as —YZ/VQ.   (See diagrammatic definitions in the ACS Official Report published in *Chem. Eng. News*, **30**, p. 4524, 1952)

RULE 6c   Give two-letter symbols in binary compounds higher rank than one-letter symbols.   Always capitalize the twelfth lower-case letter (ell) to avoid confusion with the numeral one, writing AL for aluminum and TL for thallium, and L for the twelfth position.   Thus diatomic molecules like CuI and BeO retain the cation-anion order.

Ionic compounds, such as BaQ_2, CaQ_2, KaQ, MgG_2, NaQ, SbG_5, and SnQ_4 obviously can be *identified* as written here, without the ionic punctuation, when the exact ionic nature is not specified.

7. IONS, ISOTOPES, AND STRUCTURAL UNCERTAINTIES

RULE 7a   Indicate ionic charges with the customary superscript, always with an algebraic sign (or ^{m} for minus and ^{p} for plus if the signs are not available).   Characterize odd-electron free radicals by a zero superscript, free valences by a hyphen (see Tables), and activated molecular centers by a suffixed asterisk.

Thus the cation

OH—S—CH_2CH_2—$S(CH_2CH_2$—$OH)_2^{+1}$ is denoted $QS2S2Q2Q^{p1}$

and the tributylmethyl free radical (n-$Bu_3C.$) is denoted $4Y^04.4$.

Examples of other variations are given under "Punctuation Marks" in Chapter 3, page 24.

RULE 7b Distinguish labelled atoms or atomic groups by "tagging" them with the sharp mark ♯, followed by the isotope superscript if this is known.

Thus

S^{35}-labelled NH_2—$CH(COOH)CH_2CH_2$—S^{35}—CH_3
is denoted $ZYVQ2S\#^{35}1$

S-labelled $[O_3S$—O—$(CH_2)_{16}H][Na]$ is $WS\#O.O16.,Na$

"Carbonyl-labelled" NH_2—$CO.O$—CH_2CH_3 is $ZV\#O2$

Mixed isotopic labelling may be denoted by an expanded definition of the sharp mark. Thus if the carbonyl group above were labelled with C^{14} and O^{18}, this structural information could be coded as $ZV\#O2$ $\#(C^{14},O^{18})$. Alkyl chains are split as necessary to "tag" the last C-atom in the tracer-broken chain, as in $QV1\#1$. The $H\#^2$ symbol is used for deuterium, so that the letter D can be reserved for other purposes. Thus OH—CH_2CH_2—NH—CD_3 is denoted $Q2M1H\#^2{}_3$.

RULE 7c Denote chain-linking uncertainties with hyphens and question marks.

Thus O_2N—CH_2CH_3 —$x(OH)$ is coded $WN2-?Q$

OH—$CO.CH_2CH_2$ —$CO.OH$—$(CH_3)_2$ is $QV2VQ-?1?1$

OH—$CO. \left\{ \begin{array}{l} -CCl:CH- \\ -CH:CCl- \end{array} \right\}$ —$CO.NH$—$(CH_2)_8H$

is $QV-YG:1?-VM8$

Note that Rule 2 resolves the orientation of the central segment in the last example, as well as that of the remaining parts.

RULE 7d Use condensed formula notations to identify incompletely defined salts, ions, metalloidal compounds, alloys, etc., with the generic symbol Mt for unspecified metallic atoms. Describe the *mono*substituted form of acid salts having an uncertain number of metallic cations, and show the uncertainty with an x-subscripted cation.

Thus

OH—$CO.CHOH.CO.OH(Metal)_x$ is denoted $QVYQVO.,Mt_x$

n-$C_{16}H_{33}CH(COOH).C(OH)(COOH).CH_2COOH(Na)_x$
is $QVY16.XQVQ1VO.,Na_x$

Note that Rule 2 again serves by resolving the proton-displacing uncertainty. Mixed cations, etc., in condensed formula notations are resolved by the same basic rule. Thus $(Ca,Ti)O_3$ is denoted $TiCa,.O_3$ (Ti before Ca), and $KNaCO_3$ is denoted $O_3C.,NaKa$ (Na before Ka). The condensed formulas also are used when the anionic structural details are not given. Thus borax is denoted $O_7B_4.,Na_2/.Qh_{10}$ and sodium hexametaphosphate is $O_{18}P_6.,Na_6$.

REVIEW EXERCISES

1. Identify the following common commercial chemicals (by formula or name):

AL_2G_6	$NCN.,Ca$	$O_4S.,Ca/.Qh_2$	$SS.,Fe$
$Ca,.G_2/.Qh_2$	$O_3C.,Ca$	$O_7Cr_2.,Na_2/.Qh_2$	$SSO_3.,Na_2/.Qh_5$
$Ca,.Q_2$	$O_3G.,Ka$	$O_7P_2.,Na_4/.Qh_{10}$	$ZHH,.O_3N$
$Fe,Cr,.O_4$	$O_3Si.,Na_2$	$Q_2P_2O_5.,Na_2$	$ZHH,.QVO$
$Ka,.G$	$O_4Cr.,Na_2$	$Q_2PO_2.,Na/.QH$	$ZHH,Na,.QPO_3/.Qh_4$
$Mg_2Ca,.G_6/.Qh_{12}$	$O_4G.,Na$	$QPO_3.,Na_2/.Qh_7$	$ZVO.,ZHH$
$NC.,Ka$	$O_4Mn.,Ka$	$QVO.,Na$	$ZVZ/.QQ$

2. Write systematic structure descriptions for the following commercial salts:

Anhydrite, $CaSO_4$	Limestone, $CaCO_3$
Caustic soda, $NaOH$	Pyrolusite, MnO_2
Chromite, $(Cr_2Fe)O_4$	Sal ammoniac, NH_4Cl
Copperas, $FeSO_4 \cdot 7H_2O$	Sal soda, $Na_2CO_3 \cdot 10H_2O$
Glauber's salt, $Na_2SO_4 \cdot 10H_2O$	TSP, $Na_3PO_4 \cdot 12H_2O$
Lime, CaO	Water glass, $Na_2Si_4O_9$

3. Draw the systematic graphical diagrams for the following common aldose and ketose sugars:

L-arabinose, Q1YQ//,1:O	D-glucose, Q1YQ,,/,1:O
D-erythrose, Q1YQ,,1:O	D-mannose, Q1YQ,,//1:O
L-erythrulose, Q1YQ/V1Q	D-ribose, Q1YQ,,,1:O
D-fructose, Q1YQ,,/V1Q	D-xylose, Q1YQ,/,1:O

4. Give the correctly oriented notations for the following amino acids:

L-arginine, $NH:C(NH_2)NH(CH_2)_3CH(NH_2)COOH$
L-glutamic acid, $HOCO.CH_2CH_2CH(NH_2)COOH$
L-cysteine, $HSCH_2CH(NH_2)COOH$
L-lysine, $NH_2(CH_2)_4CH(NH_2)COOH$
L-methionine, $CH_3SCH_2CH_2CH(NH_2)COOH$
L-serine, $HOCH_2CH(NH_2)COOH$

5. Make a numero-alphabetic list of the common open-chain sugars and amino acids in problems 2 and 3.

6. Convert the following postulated descriptions of organic ammonium salts to the proper indexing (base/acid) descriptions: (See Rule 10b for multi-GH)

2NH2.2,.G	ZHYVO/1VQ	ZMHYZ:M,.G
9;9MH9;9,.G	ZHYVO/1VZH,.Q	ZV1ZH,.ZVS
12MH1,.E	ZHYVO/4ZH,.G	ZVMHZ,.G
Q1XZH1Q1G,.G	ZHYVQ/4ZH,.G₂	ZVZH,.G
Q2NH2.2,.G	ZHYVQ/1SH,.OV1	ZVZH,.WNO
ZHMYZ:M,.G		

7. List the above acid/base descriptions in numero-alphabetic order and check for duplications.

8. Decode the following notations, which describe some of the most complex open-chain structures in the National Research Council's catalog of 50,000 chemicals:

1S2YZVMYVQ2S1	QV1YVQMV1MVYZ1Q
2OV1YVO2.;1VO2	QV2YVQN2CN.2CN/.QH
2OVXO2,O2.1VO2	QVY16.XQVQ1VO.,Naₓ
M:YZMY:M.N1.1/.WSQQ	WSO.YVO5.1VO5.,Na
QPQO.OYVO.:1.,Mt	

9. Are all of the above nine notations correctly oriented? (Rules 2 and 3) Draw the "unfolded" graphical diagrams of any doubtful cases.

10. List the systematic symbols for the following generic structural types:

Acids	Halides	Metallic carboxylates
Alcohols	Hydrazides	Nitriles
Aldehydes	Hydrazines	Oximes
Amides	Hydrazines,	Phenols, alkyl
Amides, alkyl	———, sym-dialkyl	Salts, amine
———, dialkyl	———, as-dialkyl	Semicarbazones
pri-Amines	Hydrazones	Sulfides
sec-Amines	Hydrocarbons	Sulfones
Esters	Ketones	Sulfonic acids
tert-Amines	Isocyanides	Sulfoxides
Ethers	Mercaptans	Ureas, alkyl

Answers:

1. Al_2Cl_6, $CaCl_2 \cdot 2H_2O$, $Ca(OH)_2$, $FeCrO_4$, KCl, $2MgCl_2 \cdot CaCl_2 \cdot 12H_2O$, KCN, $CaCN_2$, $CaCO_3$, $KClO_3$, Na_2SiO_3, Na_2CrO_4, $NaClO_4$, $KMnO_4$, $CaSO_4 \cdot 2H_2O$, $Na_2Cr_2O_7 \cdot 2H_2O$, $Na_4P_2O_7 \cdot 10H_2O$, $Na_2H_2P_2O_7$, $NaH_2PO_4 \cdot H_2O$, $Na_2HPO_4 \cdot 7H_2O$, $NaHCO_3$, FeS_2, $Na_2S_2O_3 \cdot 5H_2O$, NH_4NO_3, NH_4HCO_3, $NaNH_4HPO_4 \cdot 4H_2O$, $NH_4CO_2NH_2$, $NH_2CONH_2 \cdot H_2O$.

2. $O_4S.,Ca$, $Na,.Q$, $Fe,C_2,.O_4$, $O_4S.,Fe/.Qh_7$, $O_4S.,Na_2/.Qh_{10}$, $Ca,.O$, $O_3C.,Ca$, $Mn,.O_2$, $ZHH,.G$, $O_3C.,Na/.Qh_{10}$, $O_4P.,Na_3/.Qh_{12}$, $O_9Si_4.,Na_2$

3.
```
     Q  Q                              Q                      Q                  Q
   Q1Y—YY1:O   Q1Y—Y1:O   Q1YV1Q    Q1Y—YYV1Q    Q1Y—YYY1:O
     Q                 Q  Q                    Q  Q               Q  Q  Q

          Q  Q                                     Q
   Q1Y—YY—Y1:O    Q1Y—Y—Y1:O    Q1YYY1:O
     Q  Q                    Q  Q  Q            Q  Q
```

4.
```
   Q        Q        Q        Q        Q        Q
   V        V        V        V        V        V
  ZY3MY:M  ZY2VQ  ZY1SH  ZY4Z  ZY2S1  ZY1Q
   Z
```

5. $Q1YQ,,,1:O$, $Q1YQ,,1:O$, $Q1YQ,,/,1:O$, $Q1YQ,,//1:O$, $Q1YQ,,/V1Q$, $Q1YQ,/1:O$, $Q1YQ//1:O$, $Q1YQ/V1Q$, $ZYVQ/1Q$, $ZYVQ/1SH$, $ZYVQ/2S1$, $ZYVQ/2VQ$, $ZYVQ/3MYZ:M$, and $ZYVQ/4Z$. (This sequence is made from the above fourteen examples.)

6. $2N2.2/.GH$, $9;9M9;9/.GH$, $12M1/.EH$, $Q1XZ1Q1G/.GH$, $Q2N2.2/.GH$, $ZMYZ:M/.GH$, $ZYVQ/1VQ$, $ZYVQ/1VZ/.QH$, $ZYVQ/4Z/.GH$, $ZYVQ/4Z/.GH^2$, $ZYVQ/1SH/.QV1$, $ZMYZ:M/.GH$, $(ZV1Z/.ZVSH)$ changed to $ZVSH/.ZV1Z$, $ZVMZ/.GH$, $ZVZ/.GH$, $ZVZ/.WNQ$

7. $ZMYZ:M/.GH$ appears twice, and $ZYVQ/4Z$ appears with two proportions of GH.

8. $CH_3-S-CH_2CH_2-CH(NH_2)CO.NH-CH(CO.OH)CH_2CH_2-S-CH_3$
   $CH_3CH_2-O-CO.CH_2-C(CO.O-CH_2CH_3):CH-CO.O-CH_2CH_3$
   $CH_3CH_2-O-CO.C(O-CH_2CH_3)_2CH_2-CO.O-CH_2CH_3$
   $NH:C(NH_2)NH-C(:NH)N(CH_3)_2 \cdot H_2SO_4$
   $(OH)_2PO.OC(CO.O):CH_2 \cdot Mt$
   $OH-CO.CH_2CH(COOH)NHCO.CH_2NHCO.-CH(NH_2)CH_2-OH$
   $OH-CO.CH_2CH_2CH(COOH)N(CH_2CH_2CN)_2.H_2O$
   $n\text{-}C_{16}H_{33}CH(COOH)C(OH)(COOH)CH_2CO.ONa_x$
   $NaO_2SO.CH(CO.O-C_5H_{11})CH_2CO.O-C_5H_{11}$

9. Yes.

10.
QVA	ANA.A	ZN:A	QRxA
QA	AVOA	A	ZA/.JH
O:A	AOA	CNA	ZVMN:A
ZVA	JA	AVA	ASA
AVMA	ZMVA	SHA	WSA.A
AVNA.A	ZMA	OVA.,Mt	WSQA
ZA	AMMA	NCA	OSA.A
AMA	ZNA.A	QN:A	ZVMA

6

SYSTEMATIC CONTRACTIONS

The preceding chapters explain how open-chain structures of all kinds can be denoted diagrammatically with a logically rigorous, *additive* set of symbols — and how the diagrams in turn can be delineated in an unequivocal manner, with a minimum of writing and thinking effort. Any chemist having a working familiarity with this set of symbols will readily discover that the three *branched*-atom symbols Y, X, and K are sufficiently distinctive to permit some effort-saving contractions relating to the methyl groups, the most common of all branches. The superscripts that are required to specify ionic charges (with algebraic sign) and isotope numbers (with sharp mark) also are sufficiently distinctive to be used as multipliers of radicals and compound ions. Both types of contractions are used very frequently, hence their application becomes familiar and profitable. For example, these systematic contractions will be found applicable to *at least half* of the aliphatic compounds in large listings.

8. THE METHYL GROUP CONTRACTION *

The branched-atom symbols Y, X, and K are further defined as *methyl-branched unless otherwise specified.* The resulting symbol economies are elaborated below.

RULE 8a Apply the basic orienting Rules 2 and 3 before making any contractions; never omit the methyl symbol when it initiates the notation.

(This rule preserves the initial alphabetizing order, and prevents ambiguities)

---

* In December, 1953, Dr. W. Gruber suggested a valuable "transition" prime-marking for this contraction, described in Appendix C.

RULE 8b   Denote *isopropyl* terminals ($-CHMe_2$) and ethylidene connectives ($-CHMe.-$) with the single letter Y. (Follow punctuation Rules 3c and 3d)

Thus

$OH-CO.(CH_2)_6-CH(CH_3)_2$ is denoted QV6Y (from QV6Y1.1)

$OH-CHMe.CO.O-CHMe.CO.O-CHMe.CH_2-CHMe_2$
is QY.VOY.VOY.1Y

$(Me_2CH-)_2N-CO.CH_2CH_2CO.CH_3$
is 1Y.NV2V1.Y

Note that the last example is oriented by Rule 3e. An isopropyl *side* group requires *two* punctuation marks, since a $-Y1.1.-$ delineation is contracted in this case. The following "branched branch" examples are clarified with graphical diagrams:

$Cl_3C-CH_2CH_2-N(CHMe_2)_2$

```
                              1
                            G  Y1
is denoted GXGG2NY..Y and pictured     GX2N
                            G  Y1
                              1
```

$[Na][SCS.N(CHMe_2)_2]$

```
                            1
                            Y1
is S:YS.NY..Y.,Na          or S:Y—N .,Na
                            Y1
                            1
```

RULE 8c   Denote *tertiary butyl* terminals ($-CMe_3$) and isopropylidene connectives ($-CMe_2-$) with the single letter X. Denote the partly methylated quaternary $-CMe().-$ group with a comma punctuation (derived from $-X1,-.-$), and the *tert*-butyl side group with identical double punctuation marks.

Thus

$CH_3CH_2-O-CO.CO.CMe_3$ is denoted 2OVVX (from 2OVVX1,1.1)

$OH-CMe(CH_2CH_3).C\!:\!C-C(OH)(CHMe_2)_2$

```
                            1   Q   1
is QX,2.CCXQY..Y           or QXCCX—Y1
                            2       Y1
                                    1
```

$OH-CHMe.CMe_2.CHOH.CO.NH-CH(COOH)CH_2-CHMe_2$
is QY.X.YQVMYVQ1Y

RULE 8d Denote *trimethylammonium* terminals (—NMe₃) and —NMe₂— connectives with the single letter K. Show other variations in the same manner as with the quaternary carbon symbol X.

Thus

[CH₃—O—CO.CH₂CH₂—NMe₃][Br]
is denoted 1OV2K,.E (from 1OV2K1,1.1,.E)
[(Me₃N—CH₂)₂CHOH][Br]₂
is 1K.1YQ1K,.E₂ (see Rule 3e)

The author originally extended this general Rule 8 to include an acetyl contraction (—V for —V1), but this has been abandoned for the sake of simplicity.

9. BRANCH–PUNCTUATING CONTRACTIONS

Rule 3b specified that side groups ending with strictly terminal symbols such as —F, —G, —Q, and —Z, need not be punctuated with a period or comma. A related punctuation omission for certain methyl-branched Y, X, or K groups also is free from ambiguity if defined as stated below, and these systematic contractions help furnish *more lucid* delineations (i.e., more nearly like parts of the diagrams).*

RULE 9a Omit the punctuation for a methyl-branched Y, X, or K unit if it is the *only* branched atomic segment in the structure.

Thus

CH₂:CH-O—CO.CHMe.O—CO.CH₃
is denoted 1VOYVO1:1 (from 1VOY1.VO1:1)
NC—CMe₂Cl   is NCXG (from NCXG,1.1)
(OH—CH₂)₂CMe.CO.CH₃
is Q1XV1.1Q (from Q1X1,V1.1Q)
[n-C₁₆H₃₃NMe₂.CH₂CO.O—CH₂CH₃][Br]
is 16K1VO2,.E (from 16K1,1.VO2,.E)

RULE 9b Omit the punctuation for a methyl-branched Y, X, or K unit when it is the *last*-cited branched atomic segment.

* Dr. Gruber's prime marks, described in Appendix C, are still more lucid.

Thus

Cl—CH₂CH₂—O—SO.O—CHMe.(CH₂)₆H   is denoted G2OSO.OY6

NH₂—SO₂—CH₂CH₂—NH—CO.CHOH.CMe₂CH₂—OH

                      is ZSW2MVYQX1Q

Me₂CH—CH₂CH₂—O—CO.CMe(OH).CH₂—O—CO.CH₃

                      is 1Y.2OVXQ1OV1

[OH—CH₂—CHOH.CH₂—NMe₂—(CH₂)₁₂H][Cl]

                      is Q1YQ1K12,.G

10. SUPERSCRIPT MULTIPLIERS

Parentheses can be reserved as distinctive marks to enclose ring-system descriptions, and multiplier brackets generally can be avoided, by observing these extensions of Rule 4d.

RULE 10a   Use superscripts as multipliers of ions or molecules, citing the multiplier *after* the comma-period or stroke-period separation marks.

Thus

[NCNH]₂Ca   is denoted NCM.,²Ca

[(OH)₂PO.NH—CH₂—CO.O]₂Mg   is QPQO.M1VO.,²Mg

[n-C₆H₁₃CHOH.CH₂CH:CH(CH₂)₇CO.O]₂Ba

                      is QY6.2:8VO.,²Ba

(NH₂—O—CH₂—CO.OH)₂·HCl   is ZO1VQ/.²GH

Note that the superscript reflects the valence of the metallic atoms.

RULE 10b   Use superscripts as multipliers of radicals, applying to every preceding symbol back to the nearest hyphen (if any), when the superscript *replaces more than three* marks; i.e., when the full and shortened notations *differ by more than two* marks.

Thus   (CH₂:CHCH₂—O—CO.CH₂—)₂   is denoted 1:2OV²2

       (NCS—CH₂CH₂—)₂S   is NCS2²S

       (CH₃CH₂—O—CO.)₂CH—CH₂CH₂—CO.O—CH₂CH₃

                      is 2OV²Y2VO2

       (CH₃CH₂CH₂—CO.O—CH₂—)₂CMe.NO₂ is 3VO1²XNW

       (OH—CH₂CH₂—O—)₂PO.(CH₂)₁₄H   is Q2O²PO.14

       (Cl—CH₂CH₂—S—)₃CH   is G2S³Y

       (NC—CH₂CH₂)₃C—CO.CH₃   is NC2³XV1

       K₄Fe(CN)₆   is NC⁶Fe.,Ka₄

Note in the first example that the symbol for a central polymethylene connective is not "halved and doubled." Note also how Rule 3a favors these orientations. Centric unsaturation marks should be placed *before* the multiplying superscript, to avoid possible confusions in a terminating punctuation mark.

Thus

$trans$-(CH$_2$:CHCH$_2$—O—CO.CH:)$_2$ is denoted 1:2OV1:/^{2}

cis-(Cl—CH$_2$CH$_2$—O—CH$_2$CH$_2$—O—CO.CH:)$_2$
is G2O2OV1:,^{2}

Follow the period-eliminating contraction of Rule 9 * when single methyl-branched Y, X, or K segments appear within the multiplied quantity.

Thus

[(Me$_3$N—CH$_2$CH$_2$CH$_2$—)$_2$N—CH$_3$][Br]$_2$	is denoted	1K3^{2}N1,.E$_2$
(CH$_3$—CO.O—CHMe.—)$_2$	is	1VOY^2
(CH$_2$:CMe.CH$_2$—O—)$_3$PO	is	1:Y1O^{3}PO
(CH$_2$:CMe.CH$_2$—O—CH$_2$)$_4$C	is	1:Y1O1^{4}X
(CH$_3$CH$_2$—CO.O—CMe$_2$.C:)$_2$	is	2VOXC^2
(CH$_3$CH$_2$—CHMe.O—)$_2$PO.F	is	2YO^{2}PO.F
(NCS—CHMe.CH$_2$—)$_2$S	is	NCSY1^{2}S

Note that the side group punctuations must be retained for all but the last set of side groups when the quantity to be multiplied contains more than one branched atom (Rule 9b). Punctuation Rules 3c and 3d also must be observed.

Thus

(Me$_2$N—C:S.S—)$_2$CH$_2$	is denoted 1N1.Y:S.S^{2}1
[CH$_3$—CO.O—C(CH$_2$CH$_2$CH$_3$):]$_2$	is 1VOY3.:^{2}
[Me$_2$CH—N(CHMe$_2$).C:S.S—]$_2$	is 1Y.NY..Y:S.S^2
(Et$_2$N—CH$_2$CH$_2$)$_2$N—SO$_2$.CH$_2$CH$_3$	is 2N2.2^{2}NSW2
[(CH$_3$CH$_2$—O—)$_2$PS.—]$_2$O	is 2OPS,O2.^{2}O
(CH$_3$CH$_2$CH$_2$CH$_2$—O—C:S.S—)$_2$	is S:YO4.S^2
[S$_2$C—NH—CH$_2$CH$_2$CH$_2$—NH—CS$_2$][Na]$_2$	is S:YS.M^{2}3.,Na$_2$

Stereoisomeric punctuations, when doubled, logically denote "inversion" forms, not mirror images. Thus the alkyl D-tartrates are denoted AOVYQ/^{2}. Complex stereoisomers should be "spelled out" in full, to prevent possible misinterpretations.

* Or use Gruber's strictly additive prime marks (Appendix C).

RULE 10c   Use pairs of hyphens (a) to distinguish linear or "head-to-tail" polymeric repetitions from the above centrosymmetric types; and (b) to set off an asymmetric bivalent connective linked to two long and identical units.

Thus

$OH—(CH_2CH_2—O)_{12}CO.(CH_2)_{11}H$ is denoted Q-2O-^{12}V11

$NH_2—(CH_2—CO.NH)_4CH_2—CO.OH$ is Z-1VM-^{4}1VQ

$(CH_3CH_2CH_2CH_2—CHEt.CO.O—CHMe.—)_2—CO.NH—CH_2—$
                                              is 4Y2.VOY^2-VM1-

$(CH_2{:}CHCH_2—O—CO.CHMe.O—CO.—)_2—C({:}CH_2).CH_2—$
                                              is 1:2OVYOV^2-Y:1.1-

Symmetric linear polymer notations are resolved by Rule 2a, which gives the hyphen an alphabetizing rank equal to the letter L. Thus Q-2O-^{x}2Q is preferred to Q2-O2-^{x}Q. Many subtle "otherwise equal alternatives" are similarly resolved by Rule 2a.

RULE 10d   Use successions of superscripts to give cumulative multiplication.

Thus

$[(Et_2CH—CH_2—O—)_2PO.CH_2—]_2CH_2$ is denoted   2Y2.1O^{2}PO.^{2}3

$(CF_3CF_2CF_2CF_2)_3N$ is   F-XFF-^{4}-^{3}N

These superscript and hyphen combinations are seldom required, since they are not justified unless the full and shortened notations differ by *more than two* marks (Rule 10b).

In all the preceding examples of systematic contractions, note that the starting point is never changed by the multiplying operation; hence the important alphabetizing order generally is preserved with or without the effort-saving contractions. Nevertheless, the notation is not truly "systematic" unless the contraction rules are used with care and proper understanding. The large number of examples given in this chapter can be separated into coding or decoding exercises, to supplement those given below.

Tables 13 and 14 reveal the commonplace importance of the methyl-branch contractions. Proof of the practical value of Rules 8–10 rests entirely in the statistical data showing the great frequency of occurrence of these contractions.

Table 13. RADICALS CONTAINING THE ISOPROPYL CONTRACTION

Noncontracted Prefix	Recommended Name *	CONTRACTED NOTATION	
		As Prefix	As Suffix
1Y1.—	*Isopropyl*	1Y.—	—Y
1Y1.:	Isopropylidene	1Y.:	:Y
1Y1.1—	Isobutyl	1Y.1—	—1Y
1Y1.1O—	Isobutoxy	1Y.1O—	—O1Y
1Y1.1:	*Isobutylidene*	1Y.1:	:1Y
1Y1.1V—	Isovaleroyl	1Y.1V—	—V1Y
1Y1.1YZV—	Leucyl	1Y.1YZV—	—VYZ1Y
1Y1.2—	*Isopentyl*	1Y.2—	—2Y
1Y1.2O—	*Isopentyloxy*	1Y.2O—	—O2Y
1Y1.2:	*Isopentylidene*	1Y.2:	:2Y
1Y1.2::	*Isopentylidyne*	1Y.2::	::2Y
1Y1.3—	Isohexyl	1Y.3—	—3Y
1Y1.3:	*Isohexylidene*	1Y.3:	:3Y
1Y1.3::	*Isohexylidyne*	1Y.3::	::3Y
1Y1.3Y1.3Y1.3Y1.:2—	*Phytyl*	1Y.3Y.3Y.3Y.:2—	—2:Y.3Y.3Y.3Y
1Y1.4—	*5-Methylhexyl*	1Y.4—	—4Y
1Y1.C::	*Isobutylidyne*	1Y.C::	::CY
1Y1.O—	Isopropoxy	1Y.O—	—OY
1Y1.:1V—	[Senecioyl]	1Y.:1V—	—V1:Y
1Y1.:3X1,1:1.—	*Linalyl*	1Y.:3X,1:1.—	—X,1:1.3:Y
1Y1.:3Y1.:,2—	*Neryl* (6-ene)	1Y.:3Y.:,2—	—2:,Y.3:Y
1Y1.:3Y1.:/2—	*Geranyl* (6-ene)	1Y.:3Y.:/2—	—2:/Y.3:Y
1Y1.V—	Isobutyroyl	1Y.V—	—VY
1Y1.Y1.—	[*sec*-Isopentyl]	1Y.Y.—	—Y.Y
1Y1.YZV—	Valyl	1Y.YZV—	—VYZY

* Unbracketed names have been taken from the IUPAC "List of Radical Names" (1951). New terms recommended in this list are italicized.

Table 14. MISCELLANEOUS RADICALS CONTAINING
THE METHYL–BRANCH CONTRACTION

Noncontracted Prefix	Recommended Name *	CONTRACTED NOTATION	
		As Prefix	As Suffix
1:Y1.—	Isopropenyl	1:Y—	—Y:1
1:Y1.1—	*Methallyl*	1:Y.1—	—1Y:1
1:Y1.V—	*Methacryloyl*	1:Y.V—	—VY:1
1X1,1.—	*tert*-Butyl	1X.—	—X
1X1,1.1—	*Neopentyl*	1X.1—	—1X
1X1,1.V—	Pivaloyl	1X.V—	—VX
2X1,1.—	[*tert-Pentyl*]	2X.—	—X2
2Y1.—	*sec*-Butyl	2Y.—	—Y2
2Y1.O—	*sec-Butoxy*	2Y.O—	—OY2
2Y1.YZV—	Isoleucyl	2Y.YZV—	—VYZY2
3Y1.1—	*2-Methylpentyl*	3Y.1—	—1Y3
3Y1.1:	*2-Methylpentylidene*	3Y.1:	:1Y3
3Y1.C::	*2-Methylpentylidyne*	3Y.C::	::CY3
4Y1.—	*1-Methylpentyl*	4Y.—	—Y4
M:Y1.—	Acetimido*yl*	M:Y.—	—Y:M
Q1X1,1.YQV—	[*Pantoyl*]	Q1X.YQV—	—VYQX1Q
QY1.V—	*Lactoyl*	QY.V—	—VYQ
QY1.YZV—	*Threonyl*	QY.YZV—	—VYZYQ
—VY1.:,1V	*Citraconoyl*	—VY.:,1V—	—V1:,Y.V—
—VY1.:/1V—	*Mesaconoyl*	—VY.:/1V—	—V1:/Y.V—
—Y1.—	Ethylidene	—Y.—	—Y.—
—Y1.1—	Propylene	—Y.1—	—1Y.—
ZY1.V—	Alanyl	ZY.V—	—VYZ

* Unbracketed names have been taken from the IUPAC "List of Radical Names" (1951). New terms recommended in this list are italicized.

REVIEW EXERCISES

1. Expand the following descriptions of common commercial chemicals (a) to the corresponding noncontracted notations and diagrams; and (b) to the corresponding line-formula descriptions.

10⁴Si	1Y2OV1	GXGG	Q2OY	QY2:O	WNXGG
1V1:Y	1Y.1V1Y	GY1G	Q2Y	QY3	WNY
1VO2YO1	1Y.MY	GYG	Q5Y	QY5	WNYG
1VOYOV1	1Y.OY	ONO2Y	QVYQ/²	QY.1Y	ZX1Q
1XOV1	1YOV1	O:1O2Y	QVY:1	QY.Y	ZY
1Y	1Y:1	O:1Y	QX	QY.YQ	ZY1Q
1Y³N	2OYO2	Q1X	QX2	QYVO1Y	ZYVQ
1Y:1²V	2XOV1	Q1XZ1Q	QY	QYVO2	ZYVQY
1Y1OV1	2YOV1	Q1Y	QY1Q	QYVQ	ZYVQY2
1Y1V1	3YOV1	Q1Y2	QY2	WNXG	ZYVQYQ

2. Identify in the above list all (a) acids, (b) secondary alcohols, (c) aldehydes, (d) chloro-compounds, (e) esters, (f) ethers, (g) ketones, (h) nitrogen compounds, and (i) isopropyl derivatives.

3. Denote the following industrial chemicals with systematic symbols:

act-Amyl acetate	*tert*-Amyl alcohol	*sec*-Isoamyl alcohol
act-Amyl alcohol	Diisopropylamine	Isopropyl alcohol
sec-Amyl acetate	Isoamyl acetate	Isopropyl amine (*pri*-)
sec-Amyl alcohol	Isoamyl alcohol	Neopentanol
tert-Amyl acetate	*sec*-Isoamyl acetate	Tri-isopropylamine

4. Decode the following most complex open-chain examples in the NRC Test List:

1VOY.VO^2-Y.VO2-	3;Y.X3,CN.VO2
1Y.1YVQMVO2:1	GXGG2NY..Y/.GH
1Y.NV2VO2O1.Y	QY.VOY.VOY.1Y
2N2.2OVXE2.1Y	S:YZMN;Y.3N2.2
2OVX2,VO2.1;1Y	Z1VMYVZ1Y/.GH
2;Y.X4,VO2.VO2	ZV1YVQMV1MVYOV1

Encoding Answers:

3. 2Y1OV1, Q1Y2, 3YOV1, QY3, 2XOV1, QX2, 1Y.MY, 1Y2OV1, Q2Y 1Y.YOV1, QY.Y, QY, ZY, Q1X, and 1Y^{3}N.

Part Three

CYCLIC COMPOUNDS

7

BENZENE DERIVATIVES

The benzene ring is the most prominent of all cyclic structural features, being encountered in large lists as frequently as all other kinds of ring systems combined. The structure-coding chemist can take advantage of this statistical prominence through three effort-saving procedures: (1) by denoting the regular-hexagonal benzene ring with a single distinctive letter R (for *r*esonating *r*ing); (2) by classifying simple benzene derivatives (containing no other kinds of rings) as a separate part of the carbocyclic division of compounds; (3) by finally subordinating this prominent "common denominator" symbol to all other symbols, as specified in rule 11.

The "least effort" principle inspires a further unifying aim to *describe these benzene derivatives as much as possible like aliphatic structures:* delineate and punctuate the phenyl symbol R exactly like an alkyl numeral — remembering to rank it like a "lower than one" or zero, Ø, symbol; treat the phenylene connective like a poly-methylene connective, and a branched benzene segment like a branched aliphatic unit. Complex examples are delineated with the aid of two-dimensional diagrams, drawn with these same systematic symbols (but without any positional modulating marks).

Rules 11, 12, and 13 resemble Rules 1, 2, and 3 in their treatment of monovalent, bivalent, and polyvalent components. The conclud-ing section in this chapter summarizes the similarity of treatment between benzenoid and aliphatic structure descriptions, in con-trast with the distinctive treatment for all other kinds of cyclic structures.

11. PHENYL DERIVATIVES

RULE 11 Subordinate the monovalent symbol R (for the phenyl —C_6H_5 radical) to all other atomic group symbols, including the alkyl numerals.

Examples from the NRC—IUPAC Test List, containing phenyl terminals in various kinds of chains and branches, are given below. Thus

CH_3—CO.O—Hg—C_6H_5	is denoted 1VOHgR
$(CH_3CH_2)_2N$—$CH_2CH_2CH_2$—O—$CH(C_6H_5)_2$	is 2N2.3OYR.R
CH_3CH_2—O—CO.CH_2—$N(CH_2CH_3)$.C_6H_5	is 2OV1N2.R
$(OH$—CH_2CH_2—$)_2N$—C_6H_5	is Q2NR.2Q
$(C_6H_5$—O—$)_2PCl$	is ROPGOR
NH_2—$CH(CH_2CH_3)$.$C(OH)(C_6H_5)_2$·HCl	is ZY2.XQR.R/.GH

Common radicals containing the phenyl group are listed in Table 15.

Table 15. COMMON RADICALS CONTAINING
THE PHENYL GROUP *

1:YR.V—	Atropoyl	RC:	Benzylidyne
1YR.—	α-Methylbenzyl	RM—	Anilino
1YR.V—	Hydratropoyl	RMSW—	Phenylsulfamoyl
M:YR.—	Benzimidoyl	RMV—	Phenylcarbamoyl
OSR.—	Benzenesulfinyl	RMVM—	3-Phenylureido
	or Phenylsulfinyl	RN:	Phenylimino
Q1YR.V—	Tropoyl	RN:N—	Phenylazo
QR1:	[Salicylidene]	RO—	Phenoxy
QXR,R.V—	Benziloyl	RV—	Benzoyl
R—	Phenyl	RV1—	Phenacyl
R_3Si—	Triphenylsilyl	RV1:	Phenacylidene
R_3X—	Trityl	RVM—	Benzamido
R1—	Benzyl	RVM1V—	Hippuroyl
R1O—	Benzyloxy	RVN:	Benzoylimino
R1S—	Benzylthio (acyl)	RVO—	Benzoyloxy
	or Phenylthio (alkyl)	RYR.—	Diphenylmethyl
R1:	Benzylidene		or [Benzhydryl]
R1;1—	Styryl	RYR.:	[Benzhydrylidene]
R1;1V—	Cinnamoyl	WSR.—	Benzenesulfonyl
R1;2—	Cinnamyl		or Phenylsulfonyl
R1;2:	Cinnamylidene	WSR.M—	Benzenesulfonamido
R1V—	Phenylacetyl	—XR,R.—	[Benzhydrylidene]
R2—	Phenethyl	—YR.—	[Benzylidene]
R3—	3-Phenylpropyl	—YVR.—	[Phenacylidene]

* Unbracketed names have been taken from the IUPAC "List of Radical Names" (1951). New preferences are italicized.

Note that the subordination of a potentially branched ring symbol R helps to maintain notational clarity, and provides for a more efficient alphabetic subdivision of this largest class of cyclic compounds. Clarity becomes increasingly important when structures become more complex than those shown here; hence the longest line of *symbols* determines the delineating path in examples like ROPGOR.

12. PHENYLENE DERIVATIVES: RING LOCANTS

"Locant" symbols are required to locate cyclic positions when the ring contains two or more branches. Such positional *relations*, as this term implies, are relative rather than absolute values, hence they are symbolized in this notation by non-numeric yet consecutively related symbols: lower-case letters. No originality is claimed for this distinctive use of lower-case letters, however, since they were used with the very same meaning dozens of years before the Geneva "enumeration" concept appeared. In 1866 Auguste Kekulé * explained benzene ring isomerism with a hexagon lettered as shown in the inset. He explained the three theoretically possible bi-substituted (*ortho, meta, para*) isomers as combinations at the *ab, ac,* and *ad* positions; the three possible tri-substituted isomers as *abc, abd,* and *ace* combinations; and the three tetra-substituted isomers as *abcd, abce,* and *abde* combinations. Kekulé also indicated these positional distinctions linearly by interposing H-atom symbols where necessary, as in $C_6HBrHBrHNO_2$ for 3,5-Dibromo-1-nitro-benzene.

The two corresponding expedients incorporated in this notation are specified in the following rule.

RULE 12 (a) Any atomic group symbol placed in *f*ront of any ring symbol is understood to be in the *f*irst position, and one immediately suffixed to the benzene ring symbol is understood to be in the *second* position. (b) In all other cases, locate the ring positions with interposed lower-case letters.

For example, use the letter *c* for the third or *meta* position and *d* for the fourth or *para*, then denote the bivalent phenylene —C_6H_4— connective as R if *ortho*-branched, as Rc if *meta*-branched, and as Rd if *para*-branched. (Visualize the identity of *d* with *p*-.)

* *Ann. Chemie,* **137**, 130–96 (1866).

Thus

ortho- I—C$_6$H$_4$—CO.O—CH$_3$	is denoted IRVO1
meta- O$_2$N—C$_6$H$_4$—CO.NH—CH$_2$—CO.OH	is WNRcVM1VQ
para- NH$_2$—CO.NH—C$_6$H$_4$—As:O	is ZVMRdAs:O
p- (CH$_3$CH$_2$)$_2$N—CH$_2$CH$_2$—O—C$_6$H$_4$—C$_6$H$_5$	is 2N2.2ORdR
m,p- Et$_2$N—C$_6$H$_4$—O—CO.NH—C$_6$H$_4$—O—CH$_3$	
	is 2N2.RcOVMRdO1
o,p- OH—CO.C$_6$H$_4$—N:N—C$_6$H$_4$—N(CH$_3$)$_2$	is QVRN;NRdN1.1

Note the preferred clarity of the —Rc— and —Rd— phenylene unit descriptions. Common radicals containing the phenylene group are listed in Table 16.

Table 16. COMMON RADICALS CONTAINING
THE PHENYLENE (C$_6$H$_4$) GROUP *

1ORdV—	Anisoyl	—N;NRxN;N—	Phenylenebisazo
1ORx—	Methoxyphenyl	QRd1YZV—	Tyrosyl
1ORx1—	Methoxybenzyl	QRdORd1YZV—	Thyronyl
1ORxM—	Anisidino	QR1—	Salicyl
1Rx—	Tolyl	QR1:	Salicylidene
1RxM—	Toluidino	QRV—	Salicyloyl
1RxSW—	Tosyl (unsubstituted)	—R—	*o*-PHENYLENE
1RxV—	Toluoyl	RRx—	Biphenylyl (Xenyl)
1R1—	2-Methylbenzyl	—VRcV—	Isophthaloyl
1Y.RdM—	Cumidino †	—VRdV—	Terephthaloyl
1Y.RdV—	*p*-Isopropylbenzoyl †	—VRV—	Phthaloyl
1Y.Rx—	Cumenyl †	ZRdRdM—	Benzidino
1Y.Rx1—	Isopropylbenzyl †	ZRdSW—	Sulfanilyl
1Y.Rx1:	Isopropylbenzylidene †	ZRV—	Anthraniloyl
2ORxM—	Phenetidino	ZVRV—	Phthalamoyl

* Taken from the IUPAC "List of Radical Names" (1951).

† These examples illustrate the methyl branch contraction (Rule 8) or cyclic methyl group contraction (Rule 18, page 73).

13. POLYSUBSTITUTED DERIVATIVES

If a ring contains more than two substituents, delineate this unit exactly like a branched open chain segment; count branches and graphical symbols as the "main chain" components, and disregard directional punctuations and positional locant letters. Rule 13 extends this procedure to include benzene "branches." (See summary on page 74 for a full explanation of the branch-coding procedure.)

RULE 13 Delineate each multisubstituted benzene radical like a multibranched aliphatic unit, first following Rules 3 and 2, then showing all positional isomers with the *lowest* set of locants.

The ten possible sets of trisubstituted locant patterns are added parenthetically to the examples given below. The positional numbers in the line-formula descriptions are made to correspond with the correct locants.

$CH_3CH_2CH_2CH_2$—O—$CO.C_6H_3$.2-OH,3-O—CH_3

	is 4OVRQcO1	(abc) *
OH—$CO.CH_2$—S—C_6H_3.2-Cl,4-Cl	is QV1SRGdG	(abd)
NH_2—C_6H_3.2-OH,5-$CO.O$—CH_3	is ZRQeVO1	(abe) *

OH—CH_2—$CHOH.CH_2$—O—C_6H_3.2-CH_3,6-$CH_2CH:CH_2$

	is Q1YQ1OR1f2:1	(abf) *
NH_2—C_6H_3.3-OH,2-Cl (not in test list)		
	is ZRcQbG	(acb)
NC—C_6H_3.3-NH_2,4-O—CH_2CH_3	is NCRcZdO2	(acd) *
O_2N—C_6H_3.3-NH_2,5-O—$CH_2CH_2CH_3$		
	is WNRcZeO3	(ace) *

NC—C_6H_3.3-O—CH_3,6-CH:CH—$CO.O$—CH_2CH_3

	is NCRcO1f1:1VO2	(acf)

OH—CH_2—$CHOH.CH_2$—O—C_6H_3.2-$CH_2CH_2CH_3$,4-Br

	is Q1YQ1ORdEb3	(adb) *
OH—C_6H_3.3-O—CH_3,4-Br	is QRdEcO1	(adc) *

The structure-minded chemist can make lucid graphical diagrams of these examples simply by typewriting the aliphatic symbols around a partly typewritten hexagonal ring:

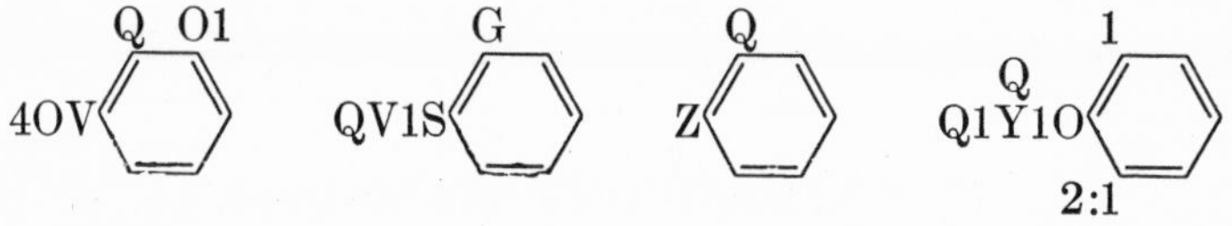

(Type the top and bottom lines and symbols in the same spacer setting along with the two stroke marks, and the mid-position symbols on a half-space setting.)

* As in aliphatic delineations, the longest sequence of atomic *symbols* forms the "main chain" which begins and ends the notation; the shortest sequences form the "side groups," regardless of their symbol rank.

Note the classifying and indexing advantages that result when, for example, the ten possible chloronitrophenols are delineated uniformly as WNRxQyG, where the values of the xy variables are bc, bd, be, bf; cb, cd, ce, cf; db (not df), and dc (not de). Each phenol theoretically "methylates" to three cresols, WNRxQyGz1, so the thirty corresponding chloronitrocresols follow the same leading sequences — with locant patterns bcd, bce, bcf; bdc, bde, bdf; bec, bed, bef; etc., for xyz.

Clarify the delineation of the more intricately branched structures by disregarding these locants and branch punctuations in the two-dimensional diagrams:

E	Q	
QRYVRE	QYR1N2	WNR1;1RO1
O Q	R 2	N O
1		W 1
QRxEyYO1.VRxQyE	QYR.RxQy1N2.2	WNRxNWy1;1RxO1yO1
QRdEbYO1.VRQ eE/.QH	QYR.RdQc1N2.2	WNRcNWd1;1RO1 cO1

The locants specified in the actual NRC–IUPAC Test List examples are given on the second line of delineations. A few of the more highly substituted examples in this Test List are delineated as shown by the analogous "X-branched" diagrams *:

G	G	G	G
GRO1R	GROVR	IRO1VO2	QR1Ø
G	G	G	Q
GR cG eG bO1R	GRG dG cOVR	IRG dG eO1VO2	QR eQ bG d1Ø

G	I	I	E
QRE	QRVO.,Na	QR1YSR	QRE
E	I	I V	Q
		Q	
QRdG bE fE	QRI dI fVO.,Na	QRI fI d1YVQSR	QRQ cE dE

I	8	$_G$G	G$_G$
QVY1RI	WNRNW	RO2O2S4	Q2OR
5 Q	Q	$_G$G	G^G
QVY5.1RdQ cI eI	WNRQ e8 cNW	GRG cG eG dO2O2S4	Q2ORG cG dG fG

In the above examples, the *optional* use of a blank space within the notation sets off each side group for instant recognizability. On the more efficient keyboards of teletype systems and punched card machinery this meaningful blank space is the "locant" operator that

* See summary on page 74.

implies *lower-case meaning* to the letter following it. Common radicals containing a polyvalent benzene ring are listed in Table 17.

Table 17. COMMON RADICALS CONTAINING
A POLYVALENT BENZENE RING *

1ORO1 d1—	Veratryl
1ORO1 d1V—	3,4-Dimethoxyphenylacetyl
1ORO1 d2—	3,4-Dimethoxyphenethyl
1ORO1 dV—	Veratroyl
1ORQ e1—	Vanillyl
1ORQ e1:	Vanillylidene
1ORQ eV—	Vanilloyl
1Rc e b—	Mesityl †
1Rc e bM—	2,4,6-Trimethylanilino †
1Rx y—	Xylyl †
1Rx yM—	Xylidino †
1Rx yV—	Dimethylbenzoyl †
1R1 d eM—	2,4,5-Trimethylanilino †
O:Rd:O b—	*p*-Benzoquinonyl
QRQ cQ eV—	Galloyl
QRQ dV—	Protocatechuoyl

* Taken from the IUPAC "List of Radical Names" (1951).
† These examples illustrate the methyl branch contraction (Rule 8) or cyclic methyl group contraction (Rule 18, page 73).

14. POLYCYCLIC CHAINS AND BRANCHES

Intricate cyclic elaborations of "branched branches," such as side groups containing branched rings, are delineated as cyclic extensions of Rule 3e. The basic aim is to picture the whole structure as a succession of branched segments.

RULE 14a Delineate all of the open-chain branches of a given ring before citing the chain leading to the next ring, and determine the "main chain" from the longest line of branched atoms or polysubstituted rings.

Thus

is a cyclic isomer of

```
       1
       O E
  QVR1RO1
       O Q
       1
```

hence is QVRO1 dO1 f1RQ eE cO1 (from the generalized QVRxO1 yO1 z1-etc.). Other examples previously given are: GRcGeGbO1R, GRGdGcOVR, QRdEbYO1.VRQeE/.QH, QRIfId1YVQSR, and WNRcNWd1;1RO1cO1.

RULE 14b Cyclic "side groups" containing rings must be punctuated with periods. (This is a "second order" complexity of branching among rings, and is relatively rare. These are the only benzocyclic examples in the Test List.)

Thus

Cl—C$_6$H$_2$. 3-Cl, 4-O—CH$_2$CH$_3$, 5-C$_6$H$_5$

is delineated GRcGeR.dO2

OH—CH$_2$CH$_2$—O—C$_6$H$_3$.2-(C$_6$H$_5$), 5-C(CH$_3$)$_3$

is Q2ORR.eX

Rule 14a would suffice to resolve these structures as GRcGdO2 eR and Q2OReX bR, but these sequences violate Rules 3a and 11. Rule 14b must be followed to clarify the delineation of cyclic "side groups" originating from an open chain atom in "branched branch" structures, even when this side group ends with a strictly terminal symbol, as in the following examples.

Cl$_3$C—CH(C$_6$H$_4$.p-Cl).O—CO.C$_6$H$_4$.o-Cl

is denoted GXGGYRdG.OVRG

Cl$_3$C—CH(C$_6$H$_4$.p-Cl).C$_6$H$_4$.p-CH$_2$CH$_2$CH$_3$

is GXGGYRdG.Rd3

OH—CO.CH$_2$CH(C$_6$H$_4$.p-Cl)$_2$ is QV1YRdG.RdG

NC—CH(C$_6$H$_4$.o-Cl)$_2$ is NCYRG.RG

RULE 14c Add *square brackets* to the punctuations for a "third order" complexity of branching, and add *braces* for a corresponding "fourth order" complexity.

No examples of these complexities are contained in the test list. If the three N atoms in 1,2,4-benzenetriamine each were joined to two dichlorophenyl groups (all different!), one specific form would be GRGcNRGfG.R[NRGdG.RGcG]dNRGeG.RGdG.

15. METALLIC SYMBOLS FOLLOWING CYCLIC SYMBOLS

Two-letter metallic or metalloidal atomic symbols cannot be confused with one-letter symbols and ring locants when the atomic symbol *precedes* the ring symbol, nor when the lower-case letter cannot represent a position in a preceding ring. When atomic symbols such as Be, Cd, Ge, Pb, Sb, or Se are cited in covalent linkage after a five- or six-membered ring symbol, the following rule prevents confusion.

RULE 15 Use hyphens to set off ambiguous two-letter atomic symbols that follow ring symbols. (Use the same punctuation for ambiguous heterocyclic symbols.)

Thus

$(Cl—C_6H_4.p-)_2Se$ is denoted GRd-Se-RdG

$(NH_2—CO.NH—C_6H_4.p-SbO_2OH)(NH_4)$

is ZVMRd-Sb-WQ.,ZHH

16. BENZOQUINONES

Benzoquinones are non-aromatic isomers of the $:C_6H_4:$ connective. Their very intimate relation with benzene derivatives and resonance isomers justifies a corresponding similarity in the symbolism, specified by the following rule.

RULE 16 Denote the *ortho-* and *para*-quinoid $:C_6H_4:$ segments by the respective symbols :R: and :Rd:, and delineate substituted derivatives like branched open-chain structures.

Thus

$O:C_6H_3.$ 2-NH—$CH_2CH_2CH_2$—N$(CH_3)_2$, 4:O

is denoted O:Rd:O bM3N1.1

$O:C_6.2,5-(OH)_2$, 3,6-Cl_2, 4:O   is O:RQeQcGfGd:O

Note that the O: group is treated exactly like any other two-mark symbol (Rule 13).

17. SUBSCRIPTS AND SUPERSCRIPTS

Cyclic extensions of the effort-saving subscript and superscript "multiplier" devices are given in the following rules of procedure, extensions of Rules 4d and 10.

RULE 17a Use subscripts as multipliers of single symbols to simplify the notation of multisubstituted rings that have no remaining unsubstituted positions.

Thus

$Cl_5—C_6.—O—(CH_2)_{12}H$ is denoted G_5RO12

$Cl_5—C_6.O—CO.CH_2—O—C_6H_3.2-Cl, 4-Cl$ is $G_5ROV1ORG$ dG

$OH—C_6.Br_5$ is QRE_5

$OH—C_6.2-CH_3.$ 3,4,5,6-Br_4 is $QR1-E_4$

The hyphen is used when a separating mark is necessary, as in the last example.

RULE 17b Use superscripts (as limited by Rule 10b) to denote the multiplication of a number of large, identical groups substituted on a ring, placing the locants *between* the ring symbol and the multiplied quantity. Omit the first locant *a* when the quantity precedes the ring symbol, and both locants when *ortho*-disubstitutions are indicated.

Thus

o-(CH$_3$CH$_2$CH$_2$CH$_2$—O—CH$_2$CH$_2$—O—CO.)$_2$C$_6$H$_4$

            is denoted 4O2OV^{2}R

[m-(Et$_3$N—CH$_2$CH$_2$—O—)$_2$C$_6$H$_4$][I]$_2$ is 2K2,2.2O^{2}cR,.I$_2$

1,4-(CH$_3$CH$_2$—O—CO.CHCN.—)$_2$C$_6$H$_2$. 2,5-(OH)$_2$

            is 2OVYCN.^{2}dRQ eQ

1,2,3-(Et$_2$N—CH$_2$CH$_2$—O—)$_3$C$_6$H$_3$ is 2N2.2O^{3}bcR

Frequently the superscript is suffixed to a ring locant to denote the point of attachment, as illustrated in these phenylene repetitions:

(CH$_3$—O—C$_6$H$_4$.m-)$_3$PO   is denoted 1ORc^{3}PO

(CH$_3$—CO.O—C$_6$H$_4$.p-)$_2$SO$_2$ is 1VORd^{2}SW

(CH$_3$CH$_2$CH$_2$CH$_2$—NH—CH$_2$—C$_6$H$_4$.p-)$_2$ ·2HCl

            is 4M1Rd^2/.GH^2

(n-C$_5$H$_{11}$—NH—CH$_2$—C$_6$H$_4$.p-)$_2$CH$_2$ is 5M1Rd^{2}1

(NCS—C$_6$H$_4$.p-)$_2$CH—CCl$_3$ is NCSRd^{2}YXGGG

(NH$_2$—C$_6$H$_4$.p-)$_2$AsO.OH   is ZRd^{2}AsQO

The full notation for the last example would be ZRdAsQO.RdZ; hence the superscript use is justified because this mark *replaces more than three* marks. Note in all cases that the initial alphabetizing order remains unchanged by this multiplication.

More highly substituted examples are illustrated below, with generalized diagrams (omitting all locants) that clarify the correct delineating sequences.

		G G	3 3
2OVR—RVO2	QRVRQ	QR1RQ	QR—RQ
N N	E E	G G	Q Q
W W			
2OVRcNW d^2	QRdE b^{2}V	QRG dG f^{2}1	QRQ d3 f^2

The hyphen must be used when the multiplication is *suffixed* to the branched symbol, as in the next three examples. The last example is resolved by the longest sequence of marks in the two-dimensional diagram.

$$
\begin{array}{cc}
1 & \\
O & E \\
RO1 & G \quad RG \\
2N2OV1:Y & GX{-}Y \\
2 \quad RO1 & G \quad RG \\
O & E \\
1 & \\
\end{array}
$$

2N2.2OV1:Y-RO1dO1²   GXGGY-RcGeE²

$$
\begin{array}{cc}
1 & \\
O & \\
R1 & G \qquad G \\
GY:Y & 1OR{-}Y{-}RO1 \\
G \ R1 & G \ GXG \ G \\
O & G \\
1 & \\
\end{array}
$$

GYG:Y-R1dO1²   1ORGdG f²YXGGG

Note that the colon in the third example must be counted as a graphical mark.

18. METHYL GROUP CONTRACTION

Methyl groups are just as commonplace in cyclic branches as they are in aliphatic branches, so a simple extension of Rule 8 is specified here.

RULE 18 All methyl branches, in any cyclic positions except the first, are denoted by the locant letter alone. If a methyl group is cited immediately after the benzene ring symbol, the unit numeral is preferred to the *b* locant.

Methyl-group locants often are the last symbols (contractions) to be cited:

NC—C$_6$H$_4$,*p*-CH$_3$	is contracted to	NCRd	(from NCRd1)
OCN—C$_6$H$_4$.*m*-CH$_3$	is	OCNRc	(from OCNRc1)
OH—CH$_2$CH$_2$—O—C$_6$H$_4$.*x*-CH$_3$	is	Q2ORx	(from Q2ORx1)

Methyl groups are the last of the single-mark aliphatic groups to be indicated:

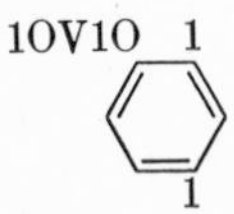

1OV1O 1   G2OV 1   Q   QV Q

1OV1OR1 d 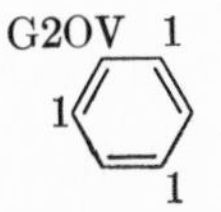   G2OVR1df 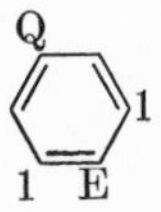   QRdEce 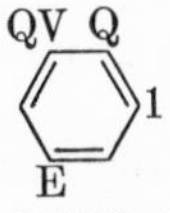   QVRQeEc

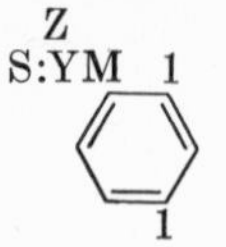

S:YZMR1d

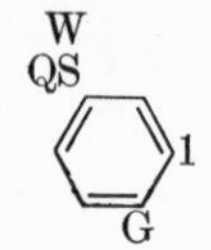

WSQRdGc

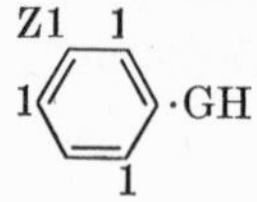

Z1R1df/·GH

However, when two or more multisymbol cyclic branches are present, these form the main line, and the methyl-group locants become "side groups," as in these cases:

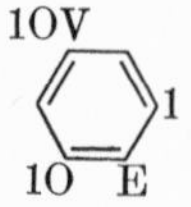

1OVRdEceO1

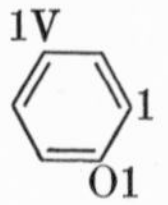

1VRcdO1

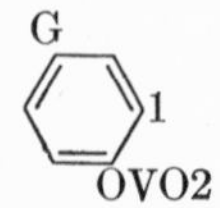

GRcdOVO2

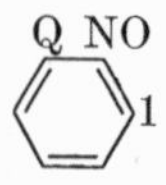

QRcbN:O

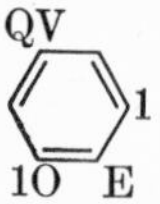

QVRdEceO1

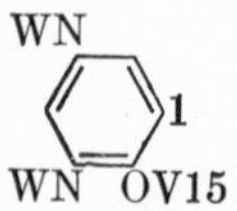

WNRceNWdOV15

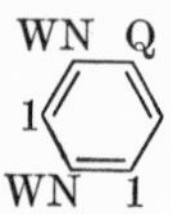

WNRQdfeNW

SIMILARITY OF PROCEDURE FOR ALIPHATIC AND BENZENOID STRUCTURE DELINEATIONS

1. Identify the longest line of branched atoms and polysubstituted rings in the structure diagram; then the longest line of marks going through these. (Note that a long linear group properly may occur between isopropyl terminals.)
2. Start delineating at the highest-ranking terminal sequence in this line.
3. At forked points, first cite the side groups having the fewest systematic marks; resolve equally short sequences by selecting the one that results in the *highest* alphabetic listing (Z before A, A before 9).
4. Identify any benzene ring positions with the *lowest* alphabetic set of locants. (The sequence *acdf* is lower than *aebd* or *adbe*).

Commonly occurring side-group symbols (and H and R) are delineated from left to right (and punctuated if not terminated by Z, W, Q, H, G, or E) in the following strictly mechanical order:

—H, Z, W, ←S, Q, ←O, ≐N, ←M, G, E, 2, 1, R, (disregard valence lines)

—VZ, VQ, VG, V2, V1, VR, :S, :M, :/2, ;2, :,2, —SH, S2, S1, O2,
O1, OR, NW, NC, MZ, MQ, M2, M1, MR, —CN, 2Z, 2Q, 2G,
2R, 1Q, 1G, 12, 1φ, 1R, RQ, RG, RdG, RcG, R2, Rd2, Rc2, R1,
Rd, Rc (Rule 18), RR, etc., with two marks;
—VVZ, VVQ, VV1, VSH, VO2, VO1, VOR, V1Z, V17, ::2, ::1, :NZ,
:/NQ, ;NQ, :,NQ, :/1G, ;1G, :,1G, SWQ, SCN, P:O, PHO, PHH,
PH2, OV2, OV1, OVR, ONW, OCN, N:O, NNN, MVZ, MV1,
MNW, HgH, HgG, CNS, CNO, 2:1, 1:S, 1;2, 1:1, etc., with three
marks;
—VVO2, VVO1, VMVZ, V2VZ, V1:O, V1:/2, V1;2, V1:,2, V1:1,
:NV1, O2:1, O1:1, MVVZ, MMVZ, AsHH, 2::2, 2::1, 2;1R,
1;1R, 1RxO1, etc., with four marks;
—VC::1, SiHHH, etc., with five marks;
—V8;3;6, etc., with six marks; . . . —V8;3;3;3, etc., with eight
marks; etc.

Note that the *cis-trans* modifying marks and the ring locants are not
counted.

REVIEW EXERCISES

1. (a) Match the following "root" names with systematic names,
and the notations with line-formula or diagrammatic descriptions.
(b) Which identifications are preferred for punched card catalogs?

Biphenyl, RR	Durene, 1R1 d e	Prehnitene, 1R1 c d
Bistyryl, R1;2;1R	Hemimellitene, 1R1 c	Pseudocumene, 1R1 d
Cumene, 1YR	Isodurene, 1R1 c e	Stilbene, R1:/1R
p-Cymene, 1YRd	Mesitylene, 1R c e	Styrene, 1:1R

2. (a) Which of the following hydroxybenzene derivatives are *not*
phenols (OH not directly attached to ring)? (b) Identify by
systematic name or by line-formula.

Anol, QRd1:2	Phenol, QR
Carvacrol, QR1 eY	Phloroglucinol, QRcQ eQ
Catechol, QRQ	Phlorol, QR2
Chavicol, QRd2:1	Pseudocumenol, QR1 d e
Cresol, QRx	Resorcinol, QRcQ
Cum*i*nol, Q1RdY	Saligenin, Q1RQ
Hydroquinone, QRdQ	Thymol, QRc fY
Orcinol, QRcQ e	

3. (a) Which of the following are phenol ethers? Which are aldehydes? (b) Identify with diagrams. (c) Which of these and the
above examples have active unsaturations?

Anethole, 2:1RdO1
Anisole, 1OR
Asarone, 2:1RO1dO1eO1
Creosol, QRd bO1
Cuminal, O:1RdY
Estragole, 1:2RdO1
Ethovan *, O:1RdQ cO2
Eugenol, 1ORQ e2:1

Guaiacol, QRO1
Homoanisole, 1ORx
Homoveratrole, 1ORx bO1
Isoeugenol, 1ORQ e1:2
Phenetole, 2OR
Vanillin, O:1RdQ cO1
Veratrole, 1ORO1

4. Identify the following aromatic acyl radicals with structure
diagrams:

Anisoyl— 1ORdV—
Anthraniloyl— ZRV—
Atropoyl— 1:YR.V—
Benzoyl— RV—
Cinnamoyl— R1:1V—
o-Cresotoyl— QR1 fV—
Cumoyl— 1Y.RdV—
Galloyl— QRQ cQ eV—

Gentisoyl— QR dQ cV—
Hippuroyl— RVM1V—
Hydratropoyl— 1YR.V—
Isophthaloyl— —VRcV—
Phthaloyl— —VRV—
Protocatechuoyl— QRQ dV—
Salicyloyl— QRV—

5. Translate the following to line-formula or graphical descriptions
and note which contain (a) primary, (b) secondary, and (c) tertiary nitrogen atoms.

Adrenalone, QRQdV1M1
Amphetamine, ZY1R
Aniline, ZR
Anisidine, ZRxO1
Arterenol, Z1YQRcQdQ
Benzamide, ZVR
Benzidine, ZRdRdZ
Benzocaine, ZRdVO2
Capsaicaine, 1Y1:5VM1RdQcO1
Carbanilide, RMVMR
Chloromycetin,* WNRdYQY1QMVYGG
Crotamiton, 2:1VN2.R1
Dulcin, ZVMRdO2
Egressin, 1Y.2MVORcfY

* Trade name.

Halazone, QVRSWNGG
Hordenine, QRd2N1.1
Mesidine, ZR1 d f
Nethamine, QYR.Y.N2.1
Nigelline, 1OVRcO1bM1
p-Phenetidine, ZRdO2
Pseudocumidine, ZR1de
Sestron base, R3N2.3R
Sulfamylon, ZSWRd1Z/.GH
Toluidine, ZRx

6. Describe the following commercial aromatics with systematic symbols, correctly oriented for cataloging purposes:

2,4-D, $2,4\text{-Cl}_2$—C_6H_3—O—CH_2—CO.OH
Azobenzene, C_6H_5—N:N—C_6H_5
Benzal chloride, C_6H_5—$CHCl_2$
Benzotrichloride, C_6H_5—CCl_3
Benzyl benzoate, C_6H_5—CH_2—O—CO.C_6H_5
Benzyl chloride, C_6H_5—CH_2—Cl
D D T, $(p\text{-Cl}$—C_6H_4—$)_2CH$—CCl_3
Dibutyl phthalate, $(n\text{-}C_4H_9$—O—CO.$)_2C_6H_4$
Methyl salicylate, $o\text{-}CH_3$—O—CO.C_6H_4—OH
p-Nitrophenol, OH—C_6H_4—4-NO_2
Protocatechuic ald., $1,2\text{-}(OH)_2C_6H_3$—4-CHO
Tricresyl phosphate, $(CH_3$—C_6H_4—O—$)_3PO$

7. Draw the graphical diagram of the structural component that is common to all of the following local anesthetics:

Benzocaine, ZRdVO2   Larocaine, ZRdVO1X.1N2.2
Butacaine, ZRdVO3N4.4   Procaine, ZRdVO2N2.2
Butesin, ZRdVO4   Propaesin, ZRdVO3
Cycloform, ZRdVO1Y   Tutocaine, ZRdVOY.Y.1N1.1

8. Delineate:

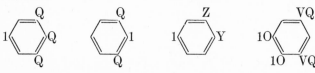

Encoding Answers:

6. QV1ORGdG, RN;NR, GYGR, GXGGR, RVO1R, G1R, GXGGYRdG.RdG, 4OVRVO4, QRVO1, WNRdQ, QRQd1:O, and 1RxO³PO.
8. QRQcQe, QRcQb, ZRebY, and QVReVQbO1cO1.

8

OTHER MONOCYCLIC COMPOUNDS

Cyclic structure descriptions in general contain new variables not found in open chain or benzenoid compounds. A cyclic compound of any kind (a) may have characteristic ring segments (carbocyclic or heterocyclic), (b) may contain one or more distinct ring systems (mononuclear or polynuclear), each of which may be monocyclic or polycyclic in structure, and (c) may have saturated, unsaturated, or "aromatic"* ring components.

The eight cyclic rules given in this chapter are paired under four headings (overall delineation, ring character, atomic groups, and linkages) in order to emphasize their associations and clarify their application to polycyclic as well as monocyclic systems.

RING–SYSTEM CLASSIFICATION AND DELINEATION

19. CYCLIC PARENTHESES

The majority of specific cyclic radicals are described so infrequently, compared with the ubiquitous benzene ring radicals, that most of these rarer compounds are characterized primarily by their ring system. The traditional classification into acyclic, carbocyclic, and heterocyclic divisions also reflects this statistical logic. Hence the

---

* A. E. Remick, in "Electronic Interpretations of Organic Chemistry," John Wiley & Sons, Inc., New York, 1943, page 152, emphasized that "There is no agreement on the definition of aromatic character (or aromaticity)." Hence the notation is designed to describe a compound's *structure*, but not to predict its complex *reactivity*.

notation for all cyclic structures other than simple benzene derivatives begins with a ring-system description.

RULE 19a Denote all cyclic structures (other than benzenoid derivatives) by starting with the description of the ring system, enclosed in parentheses. The "enclosed" ring description can be regarded as a terminal unit, to be oriented by Rule 2a with the definition that symbols within parentheses rank higher than any that are outside the parentheses.

Thus cyclohexanol is denoted (6/)aQ, not Q(6/).

RULE 19b Rank heterocyclic rings higher than carbocyclic ones; subclassify further by the number of atoms in each mononuclear system, then by the numero-alphabetic order of the symbols describing each such ring system.

Thus   (5.S) ranks higher than (6/) and higher than (5.O).
(5/O) ranks higher than (5.S)
(6/M) ranks higher than (6.N)

20. LOWEST CYCLIC MEASURES

Polycyclic systems traditionally are described in terms of the *fewest* number of *smallest* rings, and positional relations generally are resolved with the *lowest* set of locants. This "lowest value" principle for cyclic measures, which complements the *orienting* "highest first" principle of Rule 2, is generalized as Rule 20 (beginners may note that 20 is the opposite of 02!).

RULE 20 *Within the ring parentheses*, resolve all otherwise equal alternatives by selecting the sequence that gives the *lowest* possible measure of every kind — lowest polycyclic ring number, lowest ring number punctuation, lowest set of heteroatomic symbols, and lowest set of heteroatomic locants.

For example, a bicyclic system might be (56), but not (65).
Pyrazole is denoted (5.MN), not (5.NM).
Oxazole is denoted (5.NcO), not (5.NdO) nor (5.OcN).

This logical principle should be easier to remember than arbitrary lists of symbols. The most important thing to remember about ring-system descriptions is not to confuse the "highest first" orienting rule with the "lowest possible" measures that are specified within the parentheses.

RING SIZE AND NATURE

21. RING NUMBERS

Within the carbocyclic or heterocyclic divisions, ring systems traditionally are subclassified according to (1) the number of rings in the "frame" or system, and (2) the number of atomic members in each ring. Accordingly, the initial classifying mark within the parentheses is the ring number — a simple counting measure that is more useful and more definite than the "aromatic nature" of the system as a whole.

RULE 21a Punctuate each ring numeral with a "saturation" stroke mark if the indicated ring contains *more than one* saturated carbon atom (CH_2 or substituted group).

Thus

$\overline{CH_2CH_2C}(CO.O—CH_2CH_2CH_2CH_3)_2$ is denoted (3/)aVO4 aVO4

$\overline{CH_2CH_2CH_2CH_2C}:C(CN).CO.O—CH_3$ is (5/)a:YCN.VO1

$\overline{NH_2—CH—CH_2CH_2CH(CH_2CH_2CH_2CH_3)CH_2CH_2}$
is (6/)aZ d4

Note that Rule 2a (page 33) resolves the branch sequence in the last example. Table 18 (page 84) contains 15 stroke-marked examples.

RULE 21b In the absence of a stroke mark, separate the ring number from the heteroatomic symbols with a period. Omit this mark in punched-card tabulations.

Thus

$\overline{NH—C(SH):N—C(CHMe_2):CH}$ is denoted (5.McN)bSH dY

$\overline{N:C(SO_2NH_2)—CH:N—CH:CH}$ is (6.NdN)bSZW

$\overline{O—CO.CH:C(CH_3)—C(CO.OH):C—CH_3}$
is (6.OV)d eVQ f

"Aromatic" examples in Table 18 (having one or less CH_2 group) rank as follows: (5.M), (5.McN), (5.MN), (5.MN₄), (5.MNN), (5.N₄), (5.NcO), (5.NcS), (5.NO), (5.O), (5.S), (6.MdM), (6.MdS), (6.N), (6.NcN), (6.NcNeN), (6.NcO), (6.NN), and (6.O). The period merely serves to emphasize that these numerals do not represent alkyl segments; i.e., (5M) might be misunderstood to mean $(-(CH_2)_5-M-)$.

22. CYCLIC UNSATURATIONS

Nonaromatic or fixed cyclic unsaturations are shown with the colon and located with appropriate lower-case letters if they do not continue from a cited group. The often uncertain or indeterminate unsaturation locants are subordinated to better established structural features — such as the ring-fusing positions in polycyclic systems, the heterocyclic positions in monocyclic systems, or the branch positions in carbomonocyclic systems.

The old practice of determining carbomonocyclic positions from unsaturations, while apparently logical, is abandoned here in favor of a more popular recent method * which improves the structural correlations, particularly among the important terpenes and carotenes. Terpene chemists prefer not to fix carbocyclic positions by cyclic unsaturations, partly because the variable location of these active electrons generally is the least certain detail in the entire structure description.

RULE 22a Determine the locants for fixed unsaturations after all other positional relations have been resolved; and in themselves, by the *lowest* set of locants. Examples of some recommended names of *radicals,* taken from the new *CA* list,† illustrate subordination of the unsaturation positions; these relations are emphasized by showing the radical first as a suffix, then as a prefix:

2,4-cyclohexadienyl, —$\overline{CH—CH:CH—CH:CH—CH_2}$

is —(6/b:d:) or (6/b:d:)a—

3-cyclohexenylidene, :$\overline{C—CH_2CH:CH—CH_2CH_2}$

is :(6/c:) or (6/c:)a:

2-cyclopentenylidene, :$\overline{C—CH:CH—CH_2CH_2}$

is :(5/b:) or (5/b:)a:

---

* See M. W. Grafflin, "Abstracts of Papers," 116th ACS Meeting, detailed in the ACS preprint of "Joint Symposium on the Nomenclature of Hydrocarbons," Atlantic City, September, 1949.

† *C.A.* **46**, 12414 (1952).

Bis-cyclopentadienylidene, following Rule 21, is simply (5)a:(5). The corresponding *p,p'*-dihydrobiphenylene is denoted RHd:RdH (Rule 16, page 71).

RULE 22b Cite cyclic unsaturations in symbol-connecting order; omit the locants only when the unsaturation continues from a cited heteratomic group.

Thus

$\overline{\text{NH}\!-\!\text{CH}_2\!-\!\text{N}\!:\!\text{CH}\!-\!\text{CH}_2}$ (3-imidazoline) is denoted (5/McN:)

$\overline{\text{S}\!-\!\text{CH}_2\!-\!\text{N}\!:\!\text{CH}\!-\!\text{CH}_2}$ (3-thiazoline)   is   (5/NcS e:)

$\overline{\text{NH}\!-\!\text{N}\!:\!\text{CH}\!-\!\text{CH}_2\text{CH}_2\text{CO}}$ is   (6/MN: fV)

The cyclic keto and other atomic group symbols are discussed in the next section. Adjacent cyclo-allenic unsaturations (—C:C:C—) require an interposed locant to distinguish these from the equally rare cyclo-acetylenic isomers. Thus 1,2-cyclononadiene is denoted (9/a:b:) and the isomeric cyclononyne is (9/a::).

ATOMIC GROUP SPECIFICATIONS

23. OPEN–CHAIN SUBSTITUENTS

Since cyclic positions usually are determined by the ring system itself, the *simplest* and fastest method for citing the branches is to sequence them by ascending locants. This sequence then parallels the one within the parentheses.

RULE 23a Cite all *open*-chain substituents in ascending order of locants; lastly, cite the chain leading to a second ring, if any. (This rule does not apply to benzene and benzoquinone derivatives.)

RULE 23b Determine carbomonocyclic positions according to the *lowest set of locants* for all *open*-chain branches and cyclic keto, imino, or thiono groups. (Any branch leading to another ring system is not an "open" chain.)

Thus

$$OH—CO.\overset{\lceil}{C}(CH_3).CH_2CH(CHMe_2).CH_2\overset{\rceil}{C}H_2$$

is (5/)aVQ a cY   (*aV* before *a1*)

$$\overset{\lceil}{C}O.CH(CH_2CH\!:\!CHCH_2CH_3).C(CH_3)\!:\!CH—\overset{\rceil}{C}H_2$$

is (5/V c:)b2:3 c   (locants *abc*)

$$OH—\overset{\lceil}{C}H—(CHOH)_4—\overset{\rceil}{C}H—O—CH_3 \text{ (pinitol)}$$

is (6/)-Q$_5$ fO1   (Rule 17a)

$$OH—CH_2CH_2—\overset{\lceil}{C}\!:\!C(CH_3).CH_2CH_2CH_2\overset{\rceil}{C}H_2$$

is (6/a:)a2Q b   (not —a b2Q)

Note that Rule 2a resolves any otherwise equal sequences or locant alternatives. Note also that the second (b) locant is not omitted for any ring except the unusually prominent benzene ring.

24. CYCLIC ATOMIC GROUP SYMBOLS

In accordance with the graphically direct "line-formula" principle, adjacent heteratoms are cited within the parentheses in connecting order. Locants are interposed only when these symbols are not adjacent, in accordance with "least effort" Rule 1b.

Heteratoms traditionally determine the monocyclic positional relations. The selection of the *lowest*-ranking heteratomic symbol (M rather than N, etc.) is an instantly obvious operation, whereas a determination of the lowest set of locants requires counting effort. Rule 24b, which incorporates the simpler procedure, thus reduces the risk of error. This same atom-selecting principle is followed in the *C.A.* Ring Index: the lowest-ranking heteratom is given the first position even when it comes between two other heteratoms.*

RULE 24a Cite all cyclic atomic group symbols (including V and Y for unsaturated but tautomeric keto-like groups) in connecting order within the parentheses; interpose locants only when the cited segments are not adjacent.

Table 18 includes ten saturated heterocyclic examples, which would rank from lowest to highest, as follows: (5/M), (5/M)bVQ, (5/McM),

* The lowest to highest *C.A.* rank, which determines the positional numbers in the tabulated names, is: O, S, Se, Te; N, P, As, Sb, Bi; Si, Ge, Sn, Pb; B, etc., by Periodic Groups.

(5/McO), (5/McS), (5/MM), (5/MVeV), (6/M), and (6/MdO).
The corresponding line-formula descriptions are given in the Review
Exercises.

Table 18. HETEROMONOCYCLIC "PARENT" RING SYSTEMS
LISTED ACCORDING TO THE NAMES RECOMMENDED
BY THE IUPAC (1949) AND *CA* (1952)

Antipyrine	(5.NNV)a e bR	Pyrazine	(6.M dM)
Cyclotrisilane	(3-SiHH-³)	Pyrazole	(5.MN)
Cyclotrisilazane	(6-MSiHH-³)	Pyrazolidine	(5/MM)
Cyclotrisiloxane	(6-OSiHH-³)	2-Pyrazoline	(5/MN:)
Cyclotrisilthiane	(6-SiHHS-³)	Pyridazine	(6.NN)
Furane	(5.O)	Pyridine	(6.N)
Histidine	(5.McN)d1YZ/VQ	Pyrimidine	(6.NcN)
Imidazole	(5.M cN)	Pyrrole	(5.M)
Imidazolidine	(5/M cM)	Pyrrolidine	(5/M)
3-Imidazoline	(5/M cN:)	2-Pyrroline	(5/M b:)
Isoxazole	(5.NO)	Succinimide	(5/MV eV)
Morpholine	(6/M dO)	4*H*-Tetrazole	(5.N₄)
1,3-Oxazine	(6.N cO)	1,4-Thiazine	(6.M dS)
Oxazole	(5.N cO)	Thiazole	(5.N cS)
Oxazolidine	(5/M cO)	Thiazolidine	(5/M cS)
4-Oxazoline	(5/M cO d:)	3-Thiazoline	(5/N cS e:)
Pentazole	(5.M N₄)	Thiophene	(5.S)
Piperidine	(6/M)	1,3,5-Triazine	(6.N cN eN)
Proline	(5/M)bVQ	1,2,4-Triazolidine	(5/M M dM)
Pyran	(6.O)	1,2,3-Triazole	(5.M N N)

NOTE: The spaces — or half-spaces — are optional.

RULE 24b Determine heteromonocyclic positions by starting with
the *lowest*-ranking heteratomic symbol; continue in the
direction that gives the lowest set of locants for all cited
ring segments.

Thus

$\overline{\text{NH—NH—C(:NH).S—C:NH}}$ is denoted (5.MMYSY)c:M e:M

$\overline{\text{O—CO.CH:CH—CO}}$ is (5.OV eV)

$\overline{\text{NH—CO.NH—CO.C(CH}_3)(n\text{-C}_6\text{H}_{13})}$

                                                     is (5.MVMV)e6 e

$\overline{\text{NH—C(}n\text{-C}_{13}\text{H}_{27})\text{:N—CH}_2\text{CH}_2}$ is (5/M b:N)b13   (Not *bN*!)

$\overline{\text{O—SO.O—CH}_2\text{CH}_2}$ is (5/OSO)bO (acyclic O outside)

The symbol Y is used within the parentheses only to identify imino or thiono (keto-like) unsaturations, which may have enol-like tautomers.

Tautomeric equivalents of some important cyclic urea derivatives are fully elaborated and correlated as shown below, through this special use of the Y symbol.

TAUTOMERIC EQUIVALENTS (KETO–ENOLIC ISOMERISM)

Hydantoin:	(5.McNV)bQ (5.MVM)dQ (5.MVMV) (5.MVN)dQ (5.NcN)bQdQ
2-Thiohydantoin:	(5.McNV)bSH (5.MYM)b:SdQ (5.MYMV)b:S (5.MYN)b:SdQ (5.NcN)bSHdQ
Parabanic acid:	(5.McNVV)bQ (5.MVMVV) (5.MVNeV)dQ (5.NcNV)bQeQ (5.NVN)dQeQ
Barbituric acid:	(6.McNfV)bQdQ (6.McNV)bQfQ (6.McNVfV)bQ (6.MVMV)fQ (6.MVMVfV) (6.MVN)dQfQ (6.MVNfV)dQ (6.NcN)bQdQfQ (6.NVN)dQfQ
Alloxan:	(6.McNVVV)bQ (6.MVMVVV) (6.MVNeVV)dQ (6.NcNVV)bQfQ (6.NVNeV)dQfQ
Uracil:	(6.McNfV)bQ (6.McNV)bQ (6.MVMV) (6.MVN)dQ (6.MVN)fQ (6.NcN)bQdQ
Thiouracil:	(6.McNfV)bSH (6.McNV)bSH (6.MYMV)b:S (6.MYN)b:SdQ (6.MYN)b:SfQ (6.NcN)bSHdQ

When tautomers like these cannot be resolved by experimental evidence to a single choice, Rule 20 specifies that the *lowest* sequence within parentheses is preferred — the first of each above.* Barbiturates thus are coded (6.McNfV)bO dQ eA eA., Mt.

Tautomeric shifts in some cases change the ring number punctuation (Rule 21), as in the postulated enol and dienol isomers of lactide:

$$\overline{\text{O—C(OH):C(CH}_3).\text{O—C(OH):C—CH}_3}$$

is denoted (6.O dO)bQ c eQ f

$$\overline{\text{O—CO.CH(CH}_3).\text{O—C(OH):C—CH}_3} \text{ is (6.OV dO)c eQ f}$$

$$\overline{\text{O—CO.CH(CH}_3).\text{O—CO.CH—CH}_3} \text{ is (6/OV dOV)c f}$$

Since *more than one* CH_2 (or substituted) addition is required to change the period punctuation, not many examples like the lactide tautomerism will occur.

* Some chemists support the author's earlier preference *always to code the keto form*, e.g., (5.MVMV), (5.MYMV)b:S, (5.MVMVV), (6.MVMVfV).

RULE 24c   Cite the H and W symbols inside the parentheses, immediately after the symbols of the heterocyclic atoms to which they are attached.

Thus $\overline{\text{AsH—CH:CH—CH:CH}}$ is denoted (5.AsH)

            $\overline{O_2S\text{—CH}_2\text{CH:CH—CH}_2}$ is   (5/SW c:)

Table 18 also illustrates (3-SiHH-³), (6-MSiHH-³), (6-OSiHH-³), and (6-SiHHS-³).

RULE 24d   Use the symbol K to denote a fully alkylated and cationic nitrogen atom in aromatic *ternary* positions. Identify other cationic heterocyclic atoms by citing the associated unsaturation in "aromatic" positions.

Thus

$[\overline{n\text{-C}_{12}\text{H}_{25}\text{—N:C}(n\text{-C}_6\text{H}_{13})\text{—CH:CH—CH:CH}}][\text{Br}]$

                                     is (6.K)a12 b6,.E

$[\overline{O:CH\text{—CH:CH—CH:CH}}][\text{Cl}]$ is (6.O:),.G

Rare "meso-ionic" structures * like nitron and *N*-phenyl sydnone also require a distinguishing mark for the anionic atoms in these internally ionized rings. The anionic distinction is made as specified in Rule 24e.

RULE 24e   Suffix an apostrophe prime mark to the symbol or carbon-atom locant of negatively charged atoms in "meso-ionic" rings and side chains.

Thus nitron has five singly ionized resonance isomers, three of which have a cationic nitrogen atom in the first position, as shown:

$\overline{\text{CH:N}(C_6H_5).N'\text{—C}(:N\text{—}C_6H_5).N\text{—}C_6H_5}$

                      or (5.KN'dN)aR.c:NR.dR

$\overline{\text{CH:N}(C_6H_5).N:C(\text{—N}'\text{—}C_6H_5).N\text{—}C_6H_5}$

                      or (5.KN dN)aR.cN'R.dR

$\overline{\text{C}'\text{H—N}(C_6H_5):N\text{—C}(:N\text{—}C_6H_5).N\text{—}C_6H_5}$

                      or (5.KN dN e')aR.c:NR.dR

* See E. M. Crane, *Organic Chemical Bul.*, **22**, No. 2 (1950).

Note the necessary phenyl punctuations (Rule 14b, page 70). Two of the five isomers of a related thiadiazoline structure are described here. The second isomer shows how the cationic sulfur atom is identified by a suffixed colon:

CH:N(C₆H₅).N′—C(:N—C₆H₅).S̄   is delineatêd (5.KN′dS)aR.c:NR

C₆H₅—N̄—N′—C(:N—C₆H₅).S:CH
                                is (5.NN′dS:)aR.c:NR

N-phenyl sydnone also has five singly ionized resonance isomers, two of which are illustrated below. The second example shows how a prefixed colon identifies the cationic oxygen in this unusual structure:

N′—O—CO.CH:N̄—C₆H₅   is delineated (5.KN′OV)aR

C₆H₅—N̄—N:O—C(O′):CH is   (5.NN:O)dO′ aR

The apostrophe prime mark has the rank of a unit superscript — a numeral one, prefixed by a blank space. Thus the preferred *lowest sequence within the parentheses* is the first of each of the above three sets of delineations.

RULE 24f   Set off two-letter heterocyclic symbols with hyphens to avoid possible locant ambiguity when the lower-case letter might be mistaken for a locant.

Thus

SbH—S—CH₂CH(CH₂OH)—S̄   is denoted   (5/-Sb-HS eS)c1Q

but

NH—C(:N—Ag).S—CH₂C̄O   is   (5.MYS eV)b:NAg

CH₃—N̄—CO.S—C(CH₃)₂CO   is   (5.NVS eV)a d d

The last two examples illustrate the *optional* use of a printed or type-written blank space to clarify the locant-and-heteratom pairing. This blank space is essential for teletype or card-punching keyboards that have no lower-case letters.

LINKAGE SPECIFICATIONS

25. CYCLIC STEREOISOMERS

The following are cyclic extensions of Rules 5b and 5c (page 44).

RULE 25a   Orient stereoisomeric ring positions (—a—b—c—) to continue from left to right when viewed outside the ring; then punctuate the resulting "dropped" groups with a comma, and the "lifted" ones with a stroke. Resolve any starting alternatives for the open-chain branches according to Rule 2a.

Thus

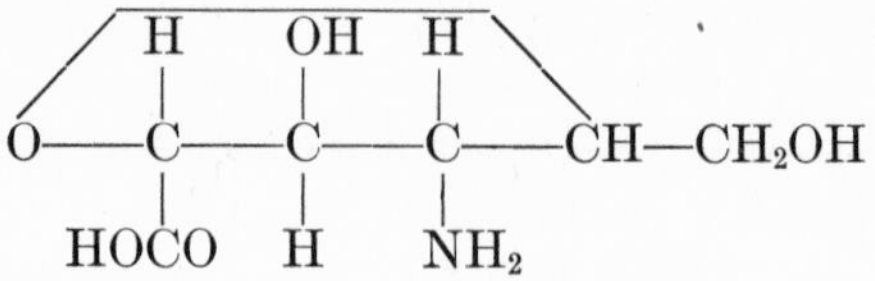

$$O\!-\!-\!C\!-\!-\!C\!-\!-\!C\!-\!-\!CH\!-\!CH_2OH$$

with H, OH, H above and HOCO, H, NH$_2$ below

is denoted $(5/O)bVQ,cQ/dZ,e1Q$

The thin connecting line is understood to be *in back of* the main line.

RULE 25b   Place the punctuation for the last-cited stereoisomeric branch *between* its locant and branch symbols, to avoid ending with a punctuation mark.

Thus

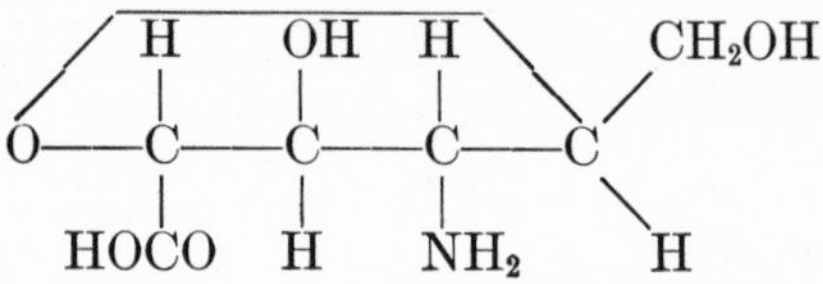

$$O\!-\!-\!C\!-\!-\!C\!-\!-\!C\!-\!-\!C$$

with H, OH, H above and CH$_2$OH / H; HOCO, H, NH$_2$ below

is denoted $(5/O)bVQ,cQ/dZ,e/1Q$

RULE 25c   Denote adjacent stereoisomeric groups by citing only the first and last of the locants (replacing the others by the stereoisomeric comma, stroke, or period); and omit the branch symbols when the adjacent groups are identical. Thus the preceding two notations can be contracted to $(5/O)bVQ,Q/Z,e1Q$ and $(5/O)bVQ,Q/Z,e/1Q$.   The second type of contraction is illustrated below:

D-glucopyranose,

$$O—CHOH—\overset{\displaystyle OH}{\underset{\displaystyle H}{C}}—\overset{\displaystyle H}{\underset{\displaystyle OH}{C}}—\overset{\displaystyle OH}{\underset{\displaystyle H}{C}}—\overset{\displaystyle H}{\underset{\displaystyle CH_2OH}{C}}$$

is (6/O)bQ./,/f,1Q

Except for Rule 2a, this could be denoted as (6/O)b1Q/cQ,/,fQ and the acyclic gluconic acid could be denoted Q1YQ,,,/,VQ to follow the orientation in the aldose, Q1YQ,,,/,1:O (the first D-determining punctuation changes sign on ring closure). Carbohydrate chemists can improve the structural correlations among these sugar derivatives by supplementing the ketonic V symbol with two "hydrogenated" and directional D or L counterparts; and by following the main-chain orientation of the aldoses in all cases. This specialized alternative notation is explained in Appendix B1.

26. CHAINS OF RINGS

Polynuclear structures (containing several ring systems) are delineated first by following the preceding rules of procedure for the initial ring-system description, then by suffixing the subordinated ring-system description through the use of a "valence bond" hyphen punctuation. The following rules apply in these cases.

RULE 26a Set off subordinated ring-system descriptions with a hyphen, and denote the point of attachment on the subordinated system with a *prefix* locant.

Thus   CH:CH—CH:N—CH:C——CH:N—CH₂CH₂CH₂
       (d :e   -f :a   -b :c)   (b :a , -e -d -c)

is denoted (6.N)c-b(5/N:)

Branches on the first ring must be cited before the *ring-linking* locants:

Thus

CH₃CH₂—N—CO.NH—CH₂.CH₂——C:CH—CH:CH—S

is (5/MVN)c2 d-b(5.S)

Likewise the symbols for any ring-linking *chain* must be cited before the hyphen:

N:CH-C(:NH)CH$_2$CH:C--SO$_2$-NH--C:N-CH:CH-CH:C-CO.NH$_2$
is (6.NcY)c:M fSWM-b(6.N)cVZ

N:CH—C(NO$_2$):CH—CH:C——O——C:N—CH:CH—CH:CH
is (6.N)eNW bO—b(6.N)

Except for the complementing Rules 20 and 2a, the last structure might be denoted as (6.N)cNW fO—b(6.N) or as (6.N)bO—b(6.N)eNW — "lowest locants," but "highest first."

The "main chain" in structures having two or more ring systems follows the *longest line of symbols* (Rule 3a), counting the constitutional parentheses and colons, but not the positional locants and branch punctuations. These branched systems are seldom met.

REVIEW EXERCISES

1. Delineate the following inorganic (carbon-free) ring structures:

Borazole, (—BH—NH—)$_3$
Cyclotrisilane, (—SiH$_2$—)$_3$
Cyclotrisiloxane, (—O—SiH$_2$—)$_3$

Pentazole, NH—N:N—N:N

2. Delineate the following completely unsaturated (aromatic or pseudoaromatic) ring derivatives:

Alloxan, NH—CO.NH—CO.CO.CO

Furane, O—CH:CH—CH:CH

Imidazole, NH—CH:N—CH:CH

Isoxazole, O—N:CH—CH:CH

Oxazole, N:CH—O—CH:CH

Pyrazine, NH—CH:CH—NH—CH:CH

Pyrazole, $\overline{\text{NH}-\text{N:CH}-\text{CH:CH}}$

Pyridazine, $\overline{\text{N:N}-\text{CH:CH}-\text{CH:CH}}$

Pyridine, $\overline{\text{N:CH}-\text{CH:CH}-\text{CH:CH}}$

Pyrimidine, $\overline{\text{N:CH}-\text{N:CH}-\text{CH:CH}}$

Pyrrole, $\overline{\text{NH}-\text{CH:CH}-\text{CH:CH}}$

1,4-Thiazine, $\overline{\text{NH}-\text{CH:CH}-\text{S}-\text{CH:CH}}$

Thiazole, $\overline{\text{N:CH}-\text{S}-\text{CH:CH}}$

Thiophene, $\overline{\text{S}-\text{CH:CH}-\text{CH:CH}}$

s-Triazine, $\overline{\text{N:CH}-\text{N:CH}-\text{N:CH}}$

v-Triazole, $\overline{\text{NH}-\text{N:N}-\text{CH:CH}}$

3. Delineate the following completely saturated (CH₂-containing) ring derivatives:

Imidazolidine, $\overline{\text{NH}-\text{CH}_2\text{NH}-\text{CH}_2\text{CH}_2}$

Morpholine, $\overline{\text{NH}-\text{CH}_2\text{CH}_2\text{O}-\text{CH}_2\text{CH}_2}$

Oxazolidine, $\overline{\text{NH}-\text{CH}_2\text{O}-\text{CH}_2\text{CH}_2}$

Piperidine, $\overline{\text{NH}-\text{CH}_2\text{CH}_2\text{CH}_2\text{CH}_2\text{CH}_2}$

Proline, $\overline{\text{NH}-\text{CH}_2\text{CH}_2\text{CH}_2\text{CH}}-\text{CO.OH}$

Pyrazolidine, $\overline{\text{NH}-\text{NH}-\text{CH}_2\text{CH}_2\text{CH}_2}$

Pyrrolidine, $\overline{\text{NH}-\text{CH}_2\text{CH}_2\text{CH}_2\text{CH}_2}$

Succinimide, $\overline{\text{NH}-\text{CO.CH}_2\text{CH}_2\text{CO}}$

Thiazolidine, $\overline{\text{NH}-\text{CH}_2\text{S}-\text{CH}_2\text{CH}_2}$

as-Triazolidine, $\overline{\text{NH}-\text{NH}-\text{CH}_2\text{NH}-\text{CH}_2}$

4. Delineate the following miscellaneous ring structures:

Antipyrine, $\overline{CH_3—N—N}(C_6H_5)CO.CH:\overset{|}{C}CH_3$

Histidine, $\overline{N:CH—NH—CH}:\overset{|}{C}—CH_2CH(NH_2)CO.OH$

Oxazine, $\overline{N:CH—O—CH}:CH—\overset{|}{C}H_2$

Pyran (4H), $\overline{O—CH:CH—CH_2CH}:\overset{|}{C}H$

Tetrazole, $\overline{N:N—N:N}—\overset{|}{C}H_2$

3-Thiazoline, $\overline{S—CH_2N:CH}—\overset{|}{C}H_2$

Encoding Answers:*

1. (6-BHM-³), (3-SiHH-³), (6-OSiHH-³), (5.MN₄).

2. (6.MVMVVV), (5.O), (5.McN), (5.NO), (5.NcO), (6.MdM), (5.MN), (6.NN), (6.N), (6.NcN), (5.M), (6.MdS), (5.NcS), (5.S), (6.NcNeNO), (5.MNN).

3. (5/McM), (6/MdO), (5/McO), (6/M), (5/M)bVQ, (5/MM), (5/M), (5/MVeV), (5/McS), (5/MMdM).

4. (5.NNV)aebR, (5.McN)dlYZ/VQ, (6.NcO), (6.O)dH, (5.N₄), (5/NcSe:).

*See Table 18, page 84.

9

BICYCLIC COMPOUNDS

Bicyclic structures constitute an especially simple type of poly-cyclic system: because only one ring junction is present, no positional isomers are possible as in the tricyclic anthracene or phenanthrene alternatives. Therefore the bicyclic ring patterns (apart from sub-stituents and unsaturations) can be described without reference to any complicating positional relations.

All possible bicyclic patterns *could* be specified completely with two numerals showing the number of atomic members in each separately considered ring, and an interposed mark or superscript showing the spiro junction or the number of atoms in the ring-fusing "bridge." Thus the following progression of two-ring designations would result from a purely mathematical or topological analysis:

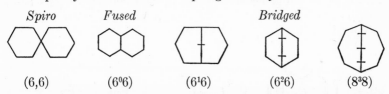

Spiro	*Fused*		*Bridged*	
(6,6)	($6^0 6$)	($6^1 6$)	($6^2 6$)	($8^3 8$)

However, this mathematical notation and classification is unsatis-factory in three important respects: (1) it fails to distinguish between aromatic and nonaromatic fused systems (spiro and bridged struc-tures are nonplanar, hence theoretically are nonaromatic); (2) it does not recognize the vast statistical prominence of fused-system compounds, and the corresponding rarity of bridged or spiro com-pounds; (3) it does not show a fundamental difference between the spiro junction and the other "bridged" junctions — apart from the risk of confusion between (6,6) and (6'6). Accordingly, the preferred notation for the rarest spiro type is longer by the addition of a ring locant (explained in Rule 29, page 99), and that for the commonest fused aromatic type is shorter by the omission of the interposed zero superscript. For typewriting convenience, the unit superscript is replaced by the apostrophe (a single prime mark), the second superscript by the ditto mark (a double prime), the third by the asterisk (a three-diagonal mark), and the fourth by the sharp ♯ (a four-line mark).

SENIORITY OR CITING AND LISTING ORDER

The order of rank of polycyclic compounds is determined first by the carbocyclic or heterocyclic nature (Rule 19), then by the multiplicity * of the system (monocyclic, bicyclic, tricyclic, etc.), and finally by the numero-alphabetic order of the marks within the parentheses. If a bicyclic structure contains two differently sized rings, the smaller ring is cited first, in order to give the smallest total ring number (Rule 20). Thus azulene is denoted (57). If the rings differ only in aromatic nature, the lower-ranking aromatic ring is cited first (Rule 21). Thus tetralin is denoted (66/). If the rings differ only in heteroatomic substituents and aromatic character, the heteratoms retain fixed locants regardless of aromatic character. If two bicyclic nuclei occur in the same structure, the higher-ranking one is cited first (Rule 2a); when the two sets of ring numbers are identical, as in quinine derivatives, fused systems are given lowest rank and spiro systems are given highest rank. Thus the six distinct types of carbocyclic 6,6-ring systems are described and ranked from lowest to highest as shown here:

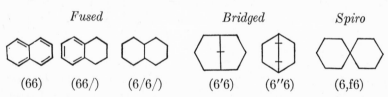

Fused			*Bridged*		*Spiro*
(66)	(66/)	(6/6/)	(6'6)	(6''6)	(6,f6)

Bicyclic structures are decidedly more numerous in the chemical literature than structures of a higher cyclic multiplicity; hence the latter are sequenced (within the major divisions) simply by the numero-alphabetic order of the marks within the parentheses.

* The "multiplicity" classification mark is an auxiliary prefixed superscript, used exactly like the "spin multiplicity" superscript in spectroscopic designations.

27. FUSED RING NUMBERS

Fused bicyclic systems contain a pair of adjacent ternary (3-coodinate) ring atoms; these form a "zero-atom bridge" and fuse the two larger bridges or loops into one system. Fused aromatic* systems, which are by far the most common bicyclic types in the literature, have the simplest bicyclic notation. However, the term "fused" is not restricted here, as it is in the older literature, only to aromatic systems: semiaromatic and nonaromatic structures also are included in this topologically homogeneous fused-ring subclass.

RULE 27a Describe *aromatic* fused-ring systems by citing the ring numbers with no intervening punctuation marks, and with no concluding period mark unless cyclic atomic letter symbols follow.

Simple carbocyclic examples are shown below. Note application of Rule 20 when the two ring numerals are different.

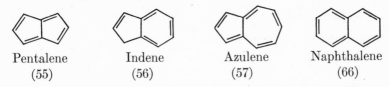

Pentalene	Indene	Azulene	Naphthalene
(55)	(56)	(57)	(66)

The alternating double bond patterns shown above (resonance isomers of many patterns) emphasize the simple bond alternation around the perimeter.

RULE 27b Describe *nonaromatic* fused-ring systems by punctuating each individually considered ring numeral with the stroke mark. Consider the shared fusion atoms to be double-bonded if one of the rings containing them is defined as aromatic.*

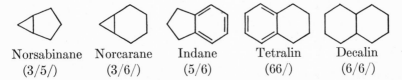

Norsabinane	Norcarane	Indane	Tetralin	Decalin
(3/5/)	(3/6/)	(5/6)	(66/)	(6/6/)

* In accordance with Rule 21 (page 80), the term "aromatic" defines rings that contain *less than two* saturated carbon atoms.

RULE 27c   Determine the positional relations by starting uniquely at one of the two fusion atoms, continuing in the direction which will give the lowest related positions to (1) the smaller ring, (2) heteroatoms, (3) aromatic atoms, (4) unsaturations, or (5) side groups.   (Compare with Rule 30)

Azabicyclic 6,6-ring examples of four types of saturation are given below:

(66.bN)   (66/bN)   (6/6.cM)   (6/6/N)

Substituted carbocyclic examples are as follows:

(56.bVdV)cV9   (5/6)Y-(6/).VO2N2.2   (66.bVeV)cSCN dG

Six heterocyclic examples are sequenced as shown:

(4/5/NVeS)   (56.bSWMV)   (56/bVMV)

(5/5/bMVM gSW)f4VQ   (66.bMVOV)hG jNW   (6/6.bOeO)h V2-(6/N)/.GH

RULE 27d   Denote nonconsecutive unsaturations by citing the higher locant as the *last* ring detail, followed by the unsaturation mark and lower locant. Thus, for example, the inset structure is denoted as (6/6/f:a).

RULE 27e   Use the hyphen to set off "aromatic" numerals larger than nine. Thus the "aromatic" 12,12-carbocyclic system is denoted (12–12).

28. BRIDGED–RING NUMBERS

Bridged bicyclic systems contain a pair of nonadjacent ternary ring atoms; that is, all three loops or bridges between these two fusing atoms contain one or more ring atoms. The smallest loop is identified as the central bridge, and the interposed superscript denotes the number of atoms in this bridge. Bridged systems must be nonplanar, hence nonaromatic structures; therefore the interposed mark also takes the place of two "saturation" stroke marks.

RULE 28a Describe bridged-ring systems by interposing a superscript or equivalent prime mark to denote the number of atoms in the smallest bridge.

The apostrophe, ditto mark, asterisk, and sharp mark are used in place of the first four superscript numerals solely because of their typewriting convenience. Carbocyclic examples of their simple application are shown below:*

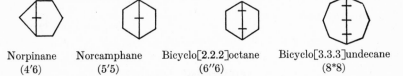

Norpinane	Norcamphane	Bicyclo[2.2.2]octane	Bicyclo[3.3.3]undecane
(4'6)	(5'5)	(6''6)	(8*8)

RULE 28b Punctuate the total ring number with a nonaromatic stroke mark only if cyclic atomic letter symbols or unsaturations follow.

The locant specifications required in these examples are determined by Rule 28c.

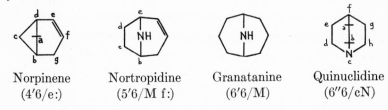

Norpinene	Nortropidine	Granatanine	Quinuclidine
(4'6/e:)	(5'6/M f:)	(6'6/M)	(6''6/cN)

RULE 28c Determine the positional relations by starting from one end of the middle bridge, continuing as specified in Rule 27c.

* The line terminals represent H atoms, not methyl groups.

Three well-known examples of heterocyclic bridged structures are described below:

Atropine
(5'6/N)a gOVYR.1Q

Quinine
(6''6/cN)e1:1 hYQ—e(66.bN)hO1

Eucalyptol
(6''6/O)b b f

RULE 28d   Distinguish stereoisomeric cyclic junctions in terms of the stereo-punctuated H-atom positions (if unsubstituted); terminate any stereoisomeric contraction with the branch symbol.

All positions are oriented and punctuated as previously explained in Rules 5b and 25. Thus the example shown in the inset is described as

$$(5'6/OcO)bH,eH,fQ,gQ/h,Q$$

29. SPIRO-RING NUMBERS

Spiro bicyclic systems contain a single quaternary atom which joins the two ring loops into a single system. The potentially stereoisomeric nature of a tetrahedral spiro atom is suggested by the interposed comma mark. Spiro rings, like bridged rings, are saturated unless otherwise noted, since true aromatic character theoretically is limited to planar configurations. The positional designations still are determined by a "longest chain" principle which is generalized in Rules 29a and 30.

RULE 29a   Prefix each ring numeral by its lowest locant unless that locant is *a*. The following simplest spiro-system examples also illustrate Rules 29b–29c.

Spiropentane   Spirohexane   Spiro(2.4)heptane   Spiro(3.3)heptane
(3,c3)   (3,c4)   (3,c5)   (4,d4)

In all of the preceding bicyclic systems, the initial locant *a* was common to both rings. However, the longest chain of ring positions (generalized as Rule 30 and followed without exception) cannot start on a spiro atom.

RULE 29b Distinguish spiro-ring systems by placing a comma between the first ring numeral and the spiro locant that precedes the second numeral.

RULE 29c Determine the positional relations by starting *next to* the spiro atom, continuing as specified in Rule 27c. Punctuate as specified in Rule 28b. Three examples are illustrated here:

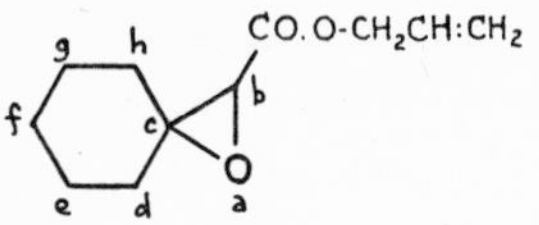

$$(3,c6/O)bVO2:1 \qquad (5,e5/OdO)fVO2 \qquad (5,e5/OfO)$$

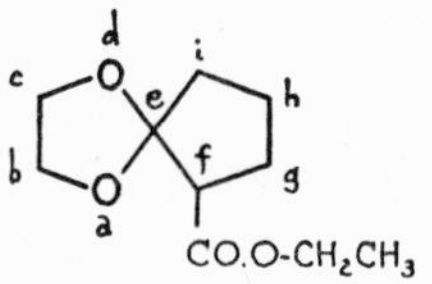

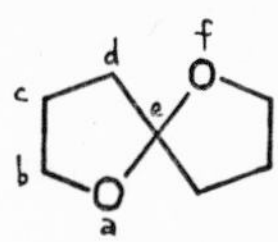

RULE 29d Distinguish stereoisomeric spiro junctions by adding a comma or stroke before the closing parenthesis: a *comma* if the stereo-orientation (Rules 5b and 25) puts the first position *below* the last position, or a *stroke* if this puts the first position *above* the last one.

For example, when the e—f—g positions in the inset diagram are viewed as a horizontal left-to-right arch, the first position appears "lower" than the last one; therefore, the comma punctuation applies.* (The heavy solid lines identify the edges that extend toward the reader.)

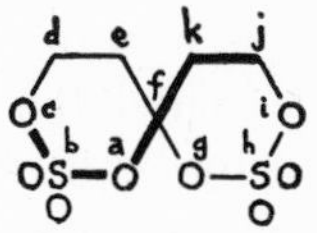

$$(6,f6/OSWO \; gOSWO,)$$

RULE 29e Give fused systems the lowest (subordinated) rank, and spiro systems the highest rank, when the cyclic nature and ring numbers are identical. Thus some previously illustrated aza-heterocyclic 6,6-ring systems are sequenced in lowest to highest order as follows:

$$(66.bN), (66/bN), (6/6.cM), (6/6/N), (6'6/M), (6''6/cN), (6,f6/bM).$$

---

* A mirror placed next to this diagram will reveal the lettered positional relations in which the stereo-stroke applies; the same reversal is obtained by exchanging the thickness of the central X-lines.

30. POLYCYCLIC POSITIONS: FUSION LOCANTS

A comprehensive generalization of polycyclic positional relations can be obtained through two effort-saving steps: (1) give adjacent ring positions consecutive locants as far as possible; and (2) start this longest chain at a mathematically unique point. The initial aim, to follow a longest possible inherently determined chain, obviously leaves the smallest number of nonconsecutive bonds that must be implied or specifically mentioned in absolutely infallible "dictionary definitions" (see Appendix B3). The concluding aim is achieved as follows: start at the point that gives the *lowest sum* for the set of *lowest positions* in each ring. This topologically unique starting point is the key to the universal position-determining Rule 30. (Obtain the smallest sum by counting one for *a*, two for *b*, and so on.)

A *fusion locant* * is the name given here for the lowest position in each ring, relative to the longest chain that starts at a unique and generally centric point.

RULE 30   Determine all polycyclic ring positions by starting the longest possible chain of ring positions at the point that gives the *lowest sum* for the fusion locants (which are the *lowest* locants in each ring).

For example, in all of the previously illustrated fused bicyclic systems, the positional chain must start at one of the two ternary fusing atoms, in order to give the lowest possible locant *a* to both rings. In bridged systems, this chain must start on the middle or smallest bridge — *next* to a ternary atom, in order to complete an unbroken chain around the perimeter. Here again, this lowest locant *a* is shared by both rings. However, in spiro "circuits," the *unshared* position next to the spiro atom must initiate the positional chain, in order to keep this locant sequence as long as possible.

The application of this position-determining rule to cyclic structures of all kinds is illustrated in the next chapter.

---

* So named because in *fused* ring patterns, but only in these, a *fusion locant* identifies a ring-fusing ternary atom.

10

POLYCYCLIC COMPOUNDS

One of the outstanding features of this notation is that the "end-to-end" chain-delineating method extends to polycyclic compounds in a simple manner: the ring numerals, like chain segments, generally describe the system with graphical directness; and the ring positions establish a longest possible chain of inherently identified connections (Rule 30).

Polycyclic ring numbers — defined exactly as in the Patterson-Capell "Ring Index," in terms of the fewest number of smallest rings — are cited in connecting order, so that a lineal 5–6–7 system is distinguished at a glance from 5–7–6 and 6–5–7 systems. The fusion locants (Rule 29a) further distinguish between angular isomers in a direct and concise manner; for example, the five possible aromatic 5,6,7-ring systems with 14 ring atoms (true lineal isomers) are lettered and delineated concisely as shown:

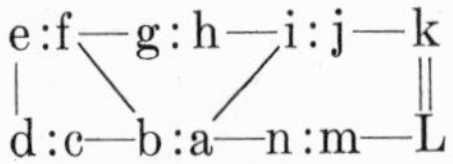

$$e:f-g:h-i:j-k$$
$$d:c-b:a-n:m-L$$
(b567)

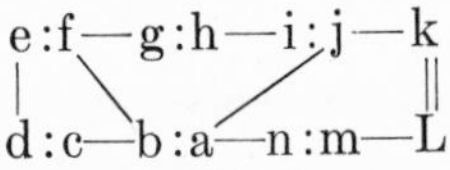

$$e:f-g:h-i:j-k$$
$$d:c-b:a-n:m-L$$
(b576)

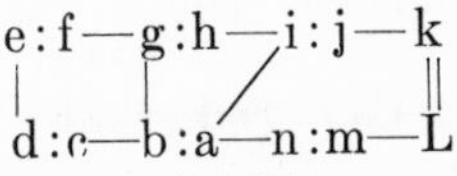

$$e:f-g:h-i:j-k$$
$$d:c-b:a-n:m-L$$
(b657)

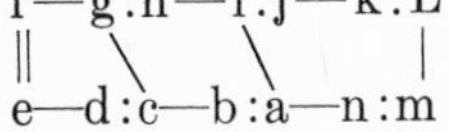

$$f-g:h-i:j-k:L$$
$$e-d:c-b:a-n:m$$
(c567)

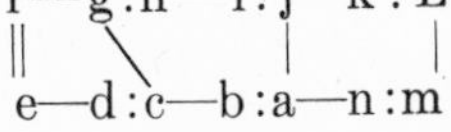

$$f-g:h-i:j-k:L$$
$$e-d:c-b:a-n:m$$
(c576)

(Note that there is no mathematical necessity to "zig-zag" the positions in the diagrams; this can be done after the whole pattern of connections is revealed.)

The "longest chain" sequence of ring positions also provides an efficient means for verifying the cyclic atom-connecting pattern in an absolute sense — through citation of the nonconsecutive bonds. For example, the absolute verifications of the above five polycyclic patterns are: (bf ai an), (bf aj an), (bg ai an), (cg ai an), and (cg aj an). These auxiliary pattern descriptions are so nearly foolproof that they can serve as "dictionary verifications" of the ring notations; therefore a systematic method for delineating the nonconsecutive bonds is given in Appendix B3.

31. PICTORIALLY DIRECT RING NUMBERS

Close correspondence with the graphical diagram is maintained through an end-to-end citation of ring numerals. Rule 31a generalizes this procedure for noncondensed systems (chains of junctions), and Rule 31b provides distinguishing marks for condensed systems (those having a fusion atom common to more than two rings). The related pictorially direct method of interposing the atomic bridge or spiro marks insures comprehension at a glance.

RULE 31a Cite the ring numbers in the pictorially direct order determined by the *ascending* sequence of *highest* locants in each ring. (Prefix the corresponding fusion locants, as specified in Rule 29, if the locant is not *a*.)

For example, the first, second, and third ring numerals in noncondensed tricyclic systems are cited from left to right as shown in the following generalized diagrams, which trace out the locant path and show nonconsecutive bonds as dotted lines:

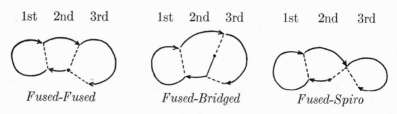

| 1st   2nd   3rd | 1st   2nd   3rd | 1st   2nd   3rd |

Fused-Fused   *Fused-Bridged*   *Fused-Spiro*

Note that the positional sequence in fused-bridged tricyclic patterns always starts on the bridge, but completes the fused terminal ring first. Likewise in fused-spiro systems, the fused terminal ring is completed first.

When the junction pattern is symmetric — as in fused-fused, bridged-bridged, or spiro-spiro junctions — the first-cited ring numeral is smaller than the third; however, this need not be the case in asymmetric junction patterns, because the lowest locant set (Rule 30) takes precedence over all other ring measures. The following three illustrated structures are examples of "inverted" sequences of ring numerals, and the notations for twelve additional inverted 5,6,7-ring systems are correlated with these as shown:

| (d6/7′5) | (c6/7,k5) | (6″7,i5) |

Fused-Bridged	*Fused-Spiro*		*Bridged-Spiro*
(c6/7′5)	(6/7,k5)	(b6/7,k5)	(6′7,j5)
(c7/5′6)	(7/5,j6)	(b7/5,j6)	(7′5,i6)
(c7/6′5)	(7/6,k5)	(b7/6,k5)	(7′6,j5)

Additional 5,6,7-ring systems are illustrated in Section 32.

Linearly fused polycyclic compounds are the types most commonly met * and easiest to delineate, since this Rule 31a also leads to a *descending* citing sequence of the *lowest* (fusion) locants in these simplest cases. Here the locant path simply follows the perimeter as in bicyclic compounds, and the resulting elongated loop is "stitched" laterally at the cited fusion atoms. Heterocyclic examples from the *Merck Index* (1952) appear below.

Carbazole	Brazilin	Berbine
(b656.hM)	(c6b5/6/6.LO)-efjoQ₄	(d6b6/6/6.kN)

---

* See statistical data on page 121.

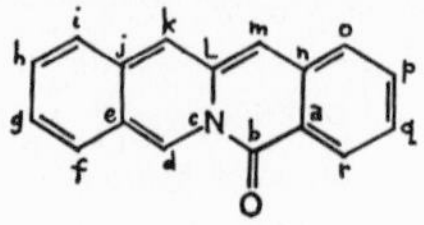

Paraberinone
(e6c666.bVN)

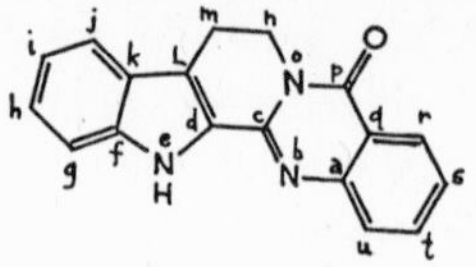

Rutecarpine
(f6d5c6/66.bNeM oNV)

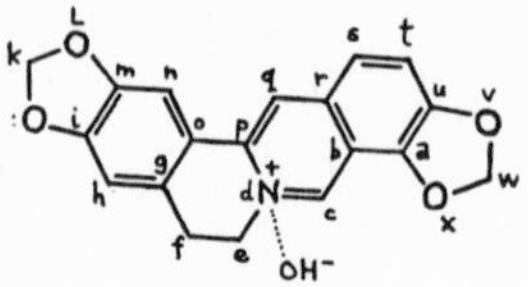

Coptisine
(i5g6d6/b665.dK-jLvxO₄),.Q

Note that the proper "lowest locant" path generally starts across an inner arc from one of the four ternary "corners," thereby reaching the furthermost ring through the shortest path. Two otherwise equal sets of locants in brazilin and rutecarpine are resolved by the five-membered ring (through Rule 20). In coptisine and in the following proposed structure for cevine, there is only one positional chain that will give the lowest set of locants, regardless of ring sizes.

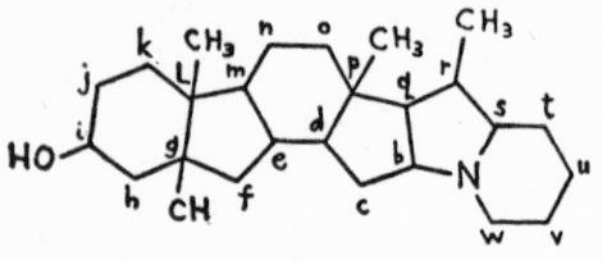

Cevine (Sabadinine)
(g6/e5/d6/b5/5/6/N)g iQ L p r

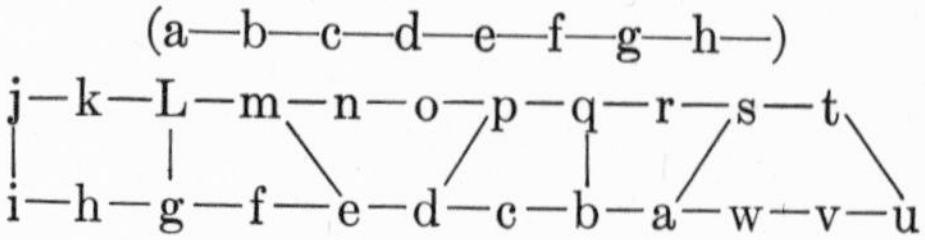

$$(a{-}b{-}c{-}d{-}e{-}f{-}g{-}h{-})$$

j—k—L—m—n—o—p—q—r—s—t

i—h—g—f—e—d—c—b—a—w—v—u

(g6/ e5/ d6/ b5/ a5/ a6/)

(gL/ em/ dp/ bq/ as/ aw/)

For example, in the ring system illustrated here, the sum of the *gedbaa* locant values is 20 (7,5,4,2,1, plus 1); whereas the corresponding sum for the next-lowest path, *hfebaa*, that would result across the top of the figure, is 23 (8,6,5,2,1, plus 1).

The right-hand figure shows how the notation can be decoded *ring by ring* in a straightforward manner if the diagram is unfolded from left to right as cited, and if the *lowest* locants are drawn *below* the highest ones (in a clockwise cycle).

Thus   g6/   means, Close a six-membered ring, starting at g.
               (g—h—i—j—k—L)

      e5/   means, Close a five-membered ring, starting at e.
               (e—f—g——L—m)

d6/   means, Close a six-membered ring, starting at d.

(d—e——m—n—o—p)

b5/   means, Close a five-membered ring, starting at b.

(b—c—d——p—q)

5/   means, Close a five-membered ring, starting at a.

(a—b——q—r—s)

6/   means, Close a six-membered ring, starting at a.

(a——s—t—u—v—w)

The first four decoding steps may be sketched as shown below:

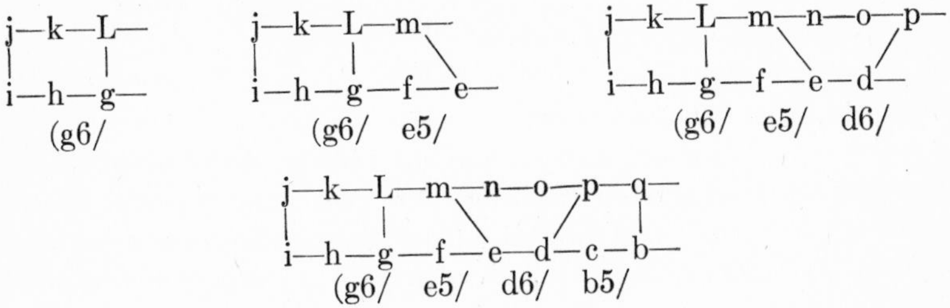

j—k—L—   j—k—L—m—   j—k—L—m—n—o—p—
| | | | \ | | \   /
i—h—g—   i—h—g—f—e—   i—h—g—f—e—d—
(g6/   (g6/   e5/   (g6/   e5/   d6/

                  j—k—L—m—n—o—p—q—
                  | | \   / |
                  i—h—g—f—e—d—c—b—
                  (g6/   e5/   d6/   b5/

A further advantage of this "longest-chain" technique with locant letters is its previously noted provision for absolutely certain, yet concise, polycyclic structure verifications — in terms of the nonconsecutive bonds. Thus the "dictionary verification" of the cevine ring-system is (gL/em/dp/bq/as/aw/N), derived as illustrated in the diagrams. The stroke mark is omitted when an individually considered ring contains less than two saturated C atoms; thus the absolute verification of the coptisine ring-system is

(im go dp/br au ax.dK—jLvxO$_4$)

Additional examples of nonconsecutive bond verifications are given in Appendix B3.

Noncondensed fused ring systems with "branched" junctions are seldom met; these cannot occur with less than four rings, just as a branched chain cannot occur with less than four atoms. In these branched fusions, the perimeter-tracing method is substantially the same as in a linear fusion, except that each branched junction interrupts the descending order of the fusion locants.

Trindene   Benzindacene   Phenanthro(9,10-c)thiophene
(b5g565)   (b5g566)   (b5g666.dS)

Tripiperideine
(b6/h6/6/6/NgNmN)

These branched fusions require three rows, rather than two, for a "ring-by-ring" interpretation of the notation. The detailed translation of (b5g566) is given in the inset. Note that an alternating double bond pattern also can be made by following this locant sequence.

$$
\begin{array}{c}
\text{h--i--j}\\
\text{e--f--g--k--L--m}\\
\text{d--c--b--a--p--o--n}\\
\text{(b5/ \quad g5/ \quad 6/6/)}
\end{array}
$$

Condensed ring systems contain atoms that are common to more than two rings. For example, *singly* condensed *fused* systems contain a ternary "triple point" atom, common to three rings; and singly condensed spiro systems contain an asymmetric quaternary atom, common to three rings. In the more common first type, the lowest-locant path always starts at this singular centric point and continues toward the furthermost ring along the shortest ring path. Condensed systems of the first (fused) type contain one atom less than the corresponding simple fused forms; this important atom-counting relation is specified in Rule 31b.

RULE 31b   Describe condensed ring systems in terms of the fewest number of smallest all-inclusive bond circuits. Cite the last and highest locant immediately after the last-cited ring number for these systems. Denote the number of

extra atom sharings (as between the first and third rings)
by suffixing a superscript (or prime mark) to the last ring
locant and punctuation.

In all fused systems the superscript denotes the number of tricyclic
ternary "triple points." In complex examples the value of the
superscript is determined by a simple arithmetic relation: the sum
of the ring numbers should equal the number of atoms in the ring
system (denoted by the last locant) plus the number of times any
"shared" atoms are counted more than once.

Thus, for example, some singly condensed spiro, fused, and bridged
5,6,7-ring systems are denoted as shown:

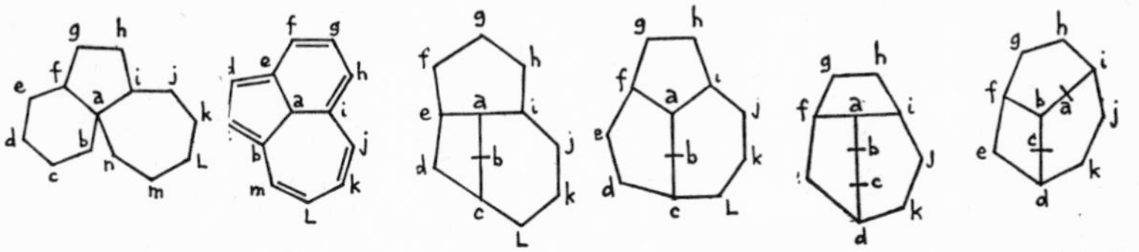

(6/5/7n/)   (567m') (5/6/7L/") (6/5/7L/") (6/5/7k/*)(b5/6'7k")

Only one fused and condensed 5,6,7-system is possible, because of
the locant path's circular symmetry. However, four different sequences of numerals are possible in the fused and singly condensed
5,6,6,6-systems (and twelve different sequences of the 5,6,6,7 numerals) because the pattern is determined primarily by the *lowest
locants*, not by the ring numerals:

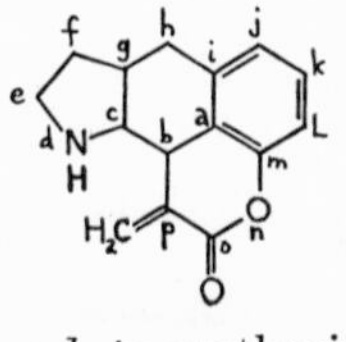

Apo-*beta*-erythroidine
(c5/6/66p'dM nOV)p:1

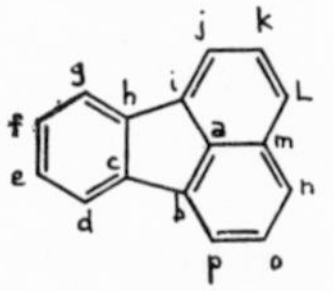

Fluoranthene
(c6566p')

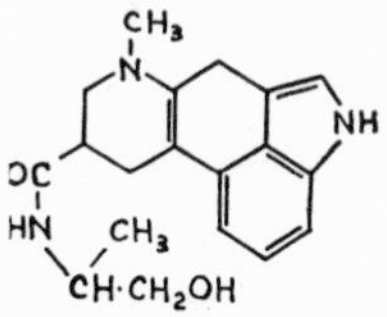

Ergonovine
(c6/6/56p'gNLMh:c)eVMY1Qg

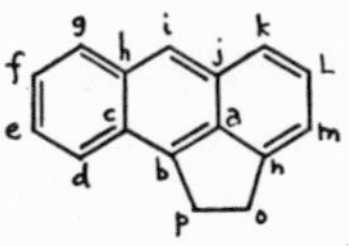

Aceanthrene
(c6665p/')

The ergonovine delineation shows how the nonconsecutive h:c unsaturation is indicated. The "ring-by-ring" translation of this tetracyclic pattern again is made with three rows of letters, as shown:

$$f-g-h-i-j-k$$
$$e-d-c-b-a-m-L$$
$$p-o-n$$

Singly condensed fused systems with more than four rings are relatively rare; three examples from the 1951 *Chemical Abstracts* Index are delineated here.*

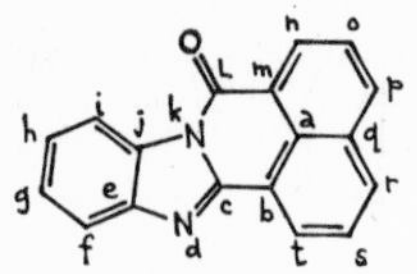

(e6c5666t'dN kNV)   (g6e5d6/665w/'fM)   (f5k5e6d6665z/'gS LVOV)
        (1)   (2)   (3)

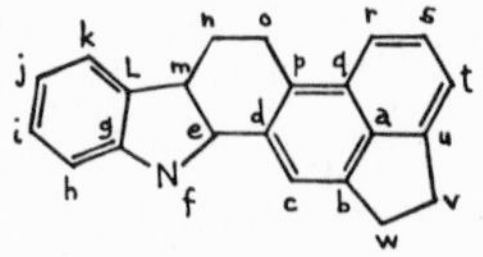

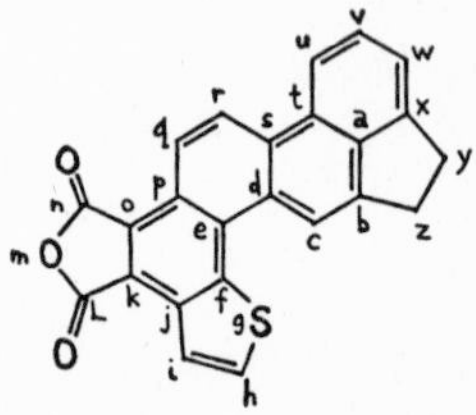

The systematic *C.A.* names for these three structures clearly illustrate the very great difficulties with present principles of polycyclic nomenclature:

(1) 7*H*-Benzimidazo(2,1-*a*)benz(*de*)isoquinolin-7-one
(2) 12*H*-Acenaphtho(4,5-*a*)carbazole, 1,2,6,7-tetrahydro-
(3) Acephenanthro(8,7-*g*)furo(3,4-*c*)thianaphthene-4,6-dione, 12,13-dihydro-

or   Acephenanthro(8,7-*g*)thianaphthene-4,5-dicarboxylic anhydride, 11,12-dihydro-.

Doubly condensed *fused* systems contain two "triple points," hence have *two* atoms less than the corresponding simple fusions, as indicated by the *double* prime:

---

* Since these rare structures are complex, the description is "verified" through the addition of the last locant.

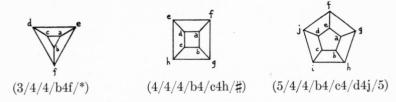

(556b6n″)   (565b6n″)   (656b5n″)   (666b6p″)
                             Pyracene   Pyrene

Note that the positional chain again starts through the two center-most points.

"Corono-fused" systems contain one or more rings that are completely enclosed by other rings. In these most highly condensed structures, the positional chain starts around the central ring, then finishes around the perimeter, generating a simple ascending order of the cited fusion locants. Thus here again the position-determining chain first passes through all of the centermost "triple points." The crystallographic forms are classical examples: the illustrated triangular prism is a *tetra*cyclic (3/4/4/b4f/*) *penta*hedron, the cube is a *penta*cyclic (4/4/4/b4/c4h/♯) *hexa*hedron, and the *octa*hedron is a *hepta*cyclic (3/3/3/3/b3/b3/c3f/*) form having the *a* position in four rings. The octahedral verification is (ac/ad/ae/eb/fb/fc/fd/).

(3/4/4/b4f/*)   (4/4/4/b4/c4h/♯)   (5/4/4/b4/c4/d4j/5)

"Cage-shaped" condensed *bridged* systems must be analyzed carefully (particularly those with *two* adjacent triple points), because the correct *lowest* ring circuits are not always obvious. Since this conceptual difficulty is inherent, no mathematical "verifications" can take the place of a careful ring analysis, preferably with several complementing diagrams. For example, the three smallest loops in the illustrated (6/7′5L′) cage structure are completed through the two tricyclic ternary atoms (black circles) as shown in the itemized locant analysis on next page. Note how clearly these ring loops can be described in terms of lower-case letters.

The cage-shaped (6/7'5L') system

The —bcd— loop through —efa— (a6)
The —ghij— loop through —kaf— (a7)
The —L— position through —efak— (a5)

Some of these "crossed-bridge" structures are apt to be confusing even to the experts. For example, in the 1950 *Chemical Abstracts* Ring Index, the inset structure was classified incorrectly as a 3,5,6,6-ring system, even though an identically related dehydrogenated derivative was classified correctly as a 3,5,5,6-ring system. The notation given by the indicated locants is (b3/5/6'5k/'cM hO). This complex bond-connecting pattern can be described with absolute certainty as (bd/af/aj/ke/), and the structure can be recognized as a singly condensed epimino-bridged type when redrawn without crossed valence lines as shown. However, no "very simple" method ever can be devised for describing very complex structures.

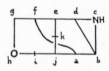

32. BRANCHED POSITIONS IN RING SYSTEMS

In a relatively small number of polycyclic systems, such as the inset adamantane structure, one or more of the positions cannot be included in the longest possible linear sequence of ring positions. These branched positions and positions beyond the twenty-sixth are specified in an unequivocal manner by the following Rule 32a. In branched locant paths the last-cited locant obviously will indicate less than the total number of ring atoms.

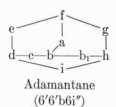

Adamantane
(6'6'b6i")

RULE 32a Designate branched cyclic positions by adding subscripts to the locant of the lowest main-line position from which the branch stems.

For example, branched positions e_1 and e_2 (stemming from position e) occur in the following two dispiro isomers:

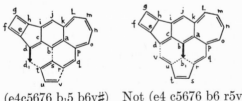

(5,e6,h7)   (5,e7,i6)

Branched positions may occur in any of the following three generalized tricyclic structure types (these diagrams supplement those shown in Section 31, page 102):

1st   2nd   3rd   1st   2nd   3rd   1st   2nd   3rd

Bridged-Bridged   *Bridged-Spiro*   *Spiro-Spiro*

The "branch" is shown as a heavy solid line in all three diagrams.

RULE 32b When alternate starting points for the longest chain are possible, choose the one that gives the lowest letter (Rule 20) for the branched locants. Apply Rule 30 by summing the branched fusion locants as decimal values.

For example, the following heptacyclic structure should be described with a branched b_1 position (not with a d_1 position as shown in the second diagram).

(e4c5676 $b_1$5 b6v$\sharp$)   Not (e4 c5676 b6 r5v$\sharp$)

Note that the incorrect alternative also leads to a much higher locant for the last cited ring.

RULE 32c Distinguish locants beyond the twenty-sixth place with primes — a′ for the twenty-seventh position, a″ for the fifty-third, and so on. Punctuate a primed last locant with the stroke or period mark to distinguish it from the "shared atom" prime mark (Rule 31b).

33. PENTACYCLIC AND HIGHER SETS OF LOCANTS

Some complex ring-fusing patterns can be described with two different sets of locants (usually from two different starting points), both of which meet the "lowest sum" requirement of Rule 30. The correct choice in such cases is determined readily by a further extension of the principle given in Rule 20.

RULE 33a When several sets of fusion locants give the same minimum sum, select the set that gives the lowest alphabetic rank (Rule 20) when sequenced as required by Rule 31a.

For example, the following fused pentacyclic system can be described with two different sets of locants (gdcaa and gebaa), both of which have the same minimum locant sum of 16 (7, 4, 3, 1, 1, and 7, 5, 2, 1, 1). However, the alphabetic sequence *gdcaa* is lower than *gebaa*, hence the first sequence alone is the correct one.

$$j—k—L—m—n—o—p—q—r—s—t$$
$$i—h—g—f—e—d—c—b—a—v—u$$
$$\text{(g7 d6 c6 a6 a5) or (g7d6c665)}$$

$$t—u—v—a—b—c—d—e—f—g—h$$
$$s—r—q—p—o—n—m—L—k—j—i$$
$$\text{Not (g5 e6 b6 a6 a7)}$$

The fusion locants (and corresponding ring numerals) must be cited in the ring-completing order specified in Rule 31a, for when structures become complex, *different sequences* of the same set of locants may describe *different ring systems*. Two such structures, verified as (dh ai am ob rc) and (dh jb am ap rc), are shown here. Note the alternating double bonds:

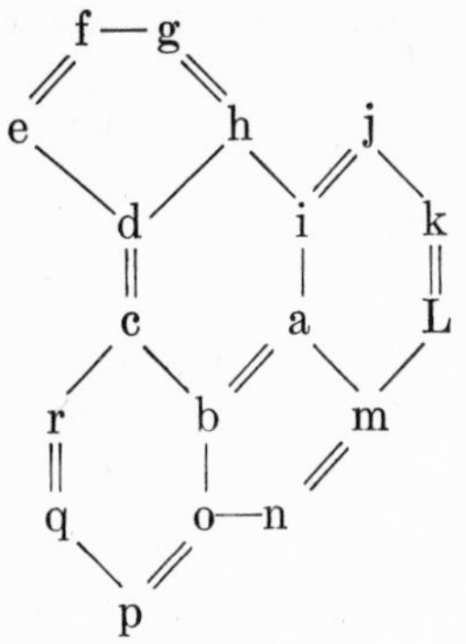

(d5   6 6 5 b6r″)
d   a a a b

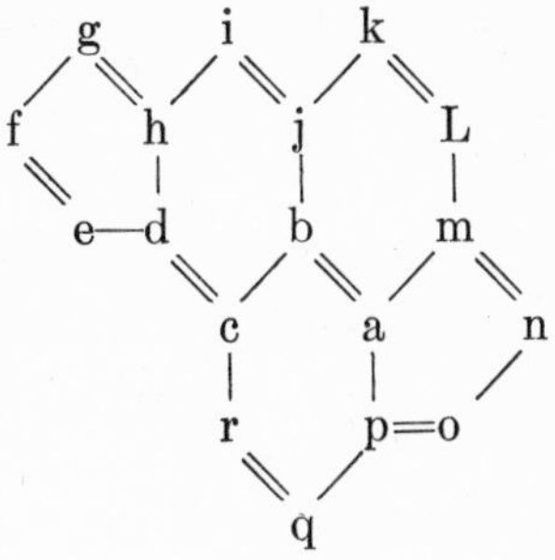

(d5   b6 6 5 6r″)
d   b a a a

Descriptions of *hexagonally* fused polycyclic systems become more clear with the following contraction, made in favor of the most commonly met ring size.

RULE 33b   Denote systems with five or more six-membered rings by citing *all* of the fusion locants plus a single numeral 6 before the last and highest locant in condensed systems.†

For example, three hexagonally fused hexacyclic structures — (ebaac6w *), (ecaaab6w *), and (ecbaaa6w *) — are denoted by the same set of locants, sequenced as shown:

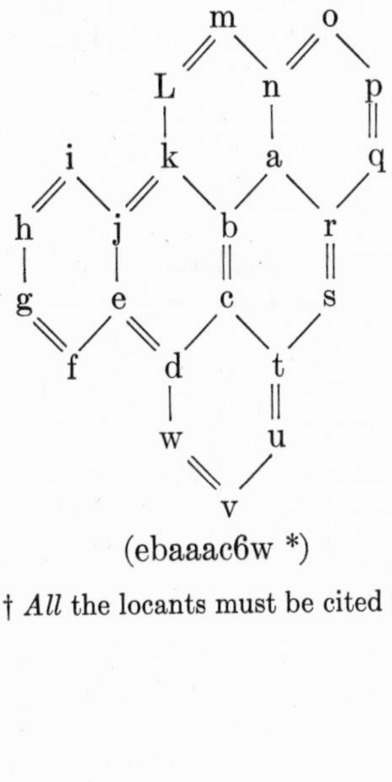

(ebaaac6w *)

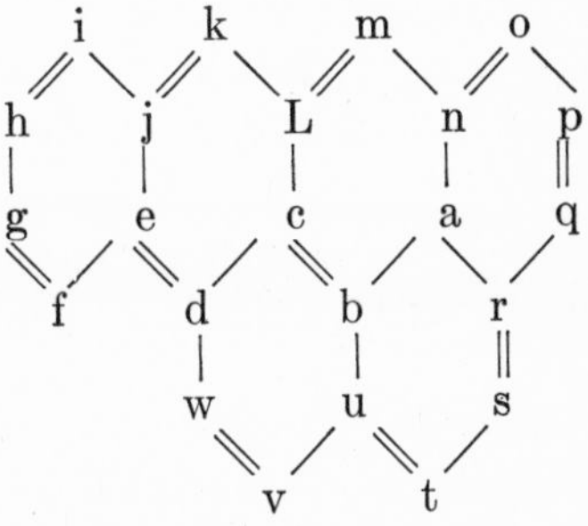

(ecaaab6w *)

† *All* the locants must be cited if any ring numerals are intermixed with them.

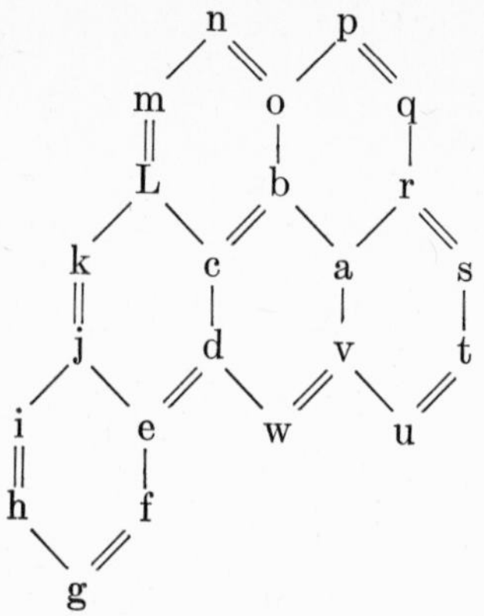

(ecbaaa6w *)

"Corono-fused" hexagonal systems can be described very concisely:

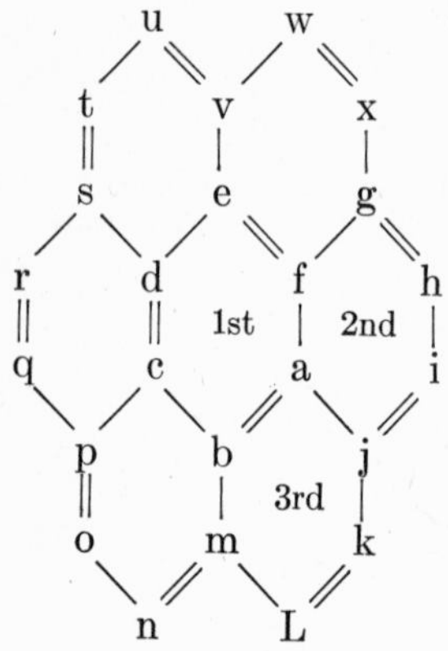

Coronene
(aaabcde6x[6])

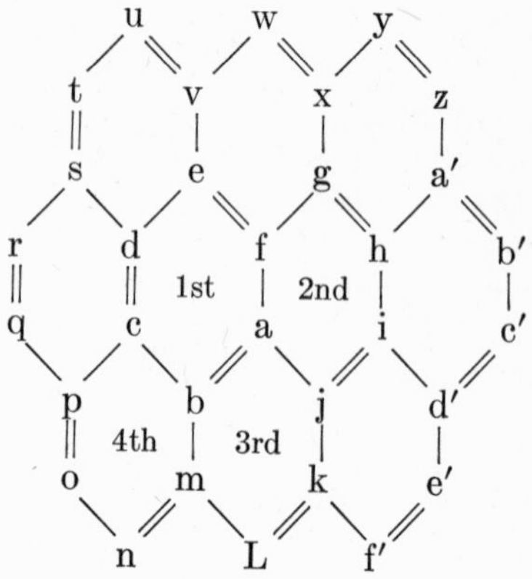

Ovalene
(aaabcdeghi6f'.[10])

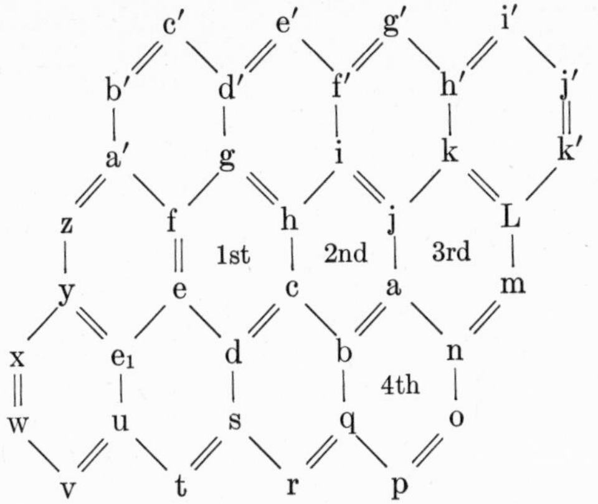

"Dodeconene"
(caaabde₁fgik6k'.¹²)

Note the similarity between the first two locant patterns. Even in the third case, note how the centermost rings are completed first, in a path that spirals outward to an alternating double bond pattern around the perimeter. Primed locants identify positions beyond the 26th. Two additional hexagonally fused structures containing the rarely encountered *branched* cyclic positions are described below.

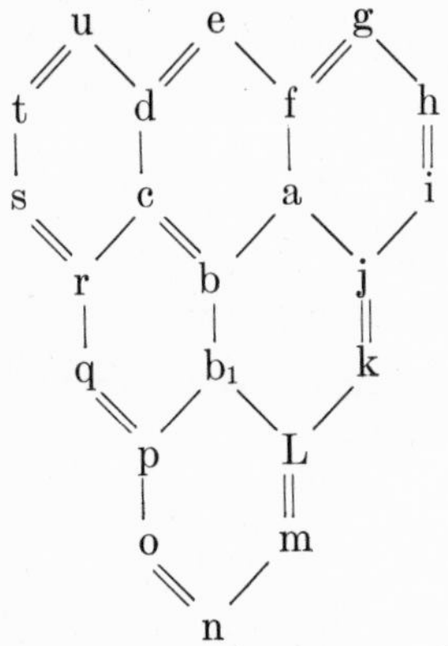

(aaab₁bc6u⁴)

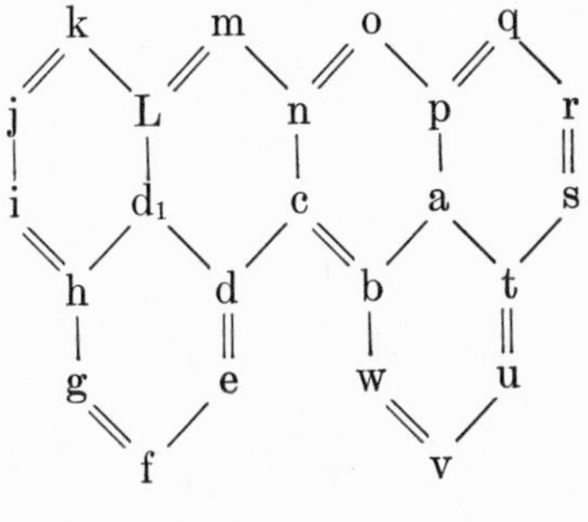

(dd₁caaa6w'')

The branched locant invariably is cited (as a fusion point) in the delineation; and in ring systems such as these, no perfect alternation of double bonds is possible.

34. SPIRO–BRIDGED RINGS AND RINGS OF RINGS

Tetracyclic and higher systems that contain "side" rings with bridged or spiro junctions require additional sets of parentheses to properly set off the interposed bridged or spiro punctuation marks. Fused polycyclic systems with "endo" bridges also can be described in terms of the unbridged part, through a similar use of additional parentheses. Likewise, large rings of rings — as in the porphyrin and curarin derivatives — can be described most readily in terms of the corresponding sequence of ring segments, enclosed in an all-inclusive set of parentheses.

RULE 34a Describe "endo-bridged" and spiro-linked extensions of fused *poly*cyclic systems in terms of the simpler fused ring system (the one with lowest locants and smallest spiro or endo linkages, if alternatives are possible). Prefix the higher bridging locant to the fused ring notation, suffix the lower locant and bridge symbols to it, then enclose the entirety in a second set of parentheses, with connective hyphens. Use the letter X instead of the first hyphen for spiro-linked adducts.

(Xe(b666)e4-)fH

Spiro "loops" are denoted as bridges that return to the same bridging locant, as illustrated by the above example, a spiro-looped phenanthrene. Diagrams should not be necessary to show that the following are "methano" endo-bridged anthracene systems:

(-g(c666)d1-), (-i(c666)b1-), (-L(c666)f1-)

Likewise, the bridge component in the related structures given here should be evident at a glance: (-g(c666)d2-), (-i(c666)b1:1-), and (-i(c666)bS-).

Additional bridges require additional parentheses, as shown in the following structure, postulated for the insecticide that is identified most conveniently by the generic name "dieldrin." This particular structure has a simple *linear* sequence of bridged and fused junctions, so the preferred description in this case is $(3/5'd5/g5'i5/bOL:)$-ijjkLmG$_6$.

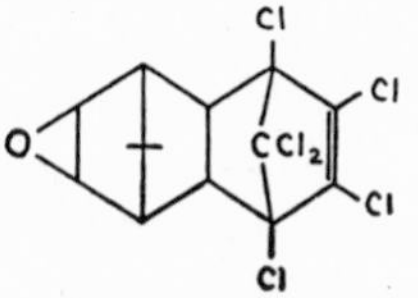

(-k(-f(c3/6/6/dOi:)1-)hXGG-)-hijkG$_4$

RULE 34b Describe large rings of rings (containing a central member of more than nine atoms) as a parenthetically enclosed "chain" of rings and branches. Start this chain description with the hyphenated higher point of attachment on the highest-ranking ring system in the closed chain (following Rule 2a). Cite side branches as previously described, inside the all-inclusive parentheses.

Thus two relatively simple structures from the Ring Index are delineated as follows. The second example shows how the description begins uniformly with a hyphen, even when this "spanning" link is a double bond.

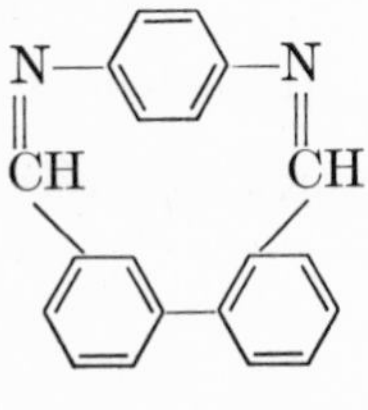

(-N:1RcRc1:NRd-) 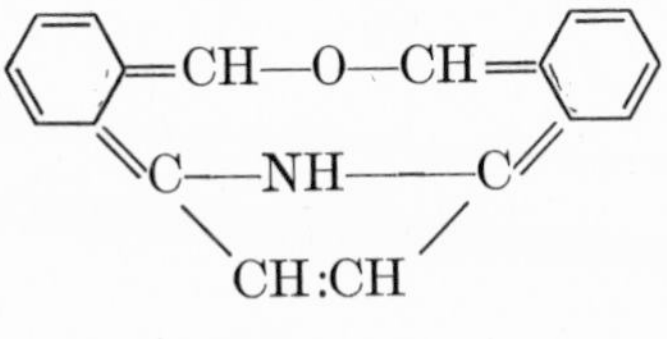   (-e(5.M):R:1O1:R:)

Note in these examples the advantages of describing the benzene rings with a simple single letter, free from unnecessary parentheses. Rule 2a determines the "highest possible" starting point in long closed chains of ring and branch segments, such as those in the illustrated hematoporphyrin structure:

(-e(5.N)cYQ d b:1-e(5.M)cYQ d b1:e(5.N)c2VQd b1:e(5.M)c2VQ d b:1-)

Note that this delineation includes two methyl-branch contractions (Rules 8 and 9) and four cyclic methyl group contractions (Rule 18).

Both of the cationic bicyclic ring components in the following tubocurarin structure are identical up to the substituent on the i positions, hence the difference at this point (between Q and O) resolves the "highest possible" orientation. The complete structure description is:

Tubocurarin

(-j(6/6.cK)hO1 iQ b1RdQ cO-i(6/6.cK)hO1 b1RdO-),.G₂

These two biological structures should put a final emphasis on the impossibility of describing very complex atomic arrangements with a very simple set of marks.

35. CHELATE RINGS (ORGANOMETALLIC COMPLEXES)

The above rules improve the recognition at a glance of the individual components in large cyclic aggregates. This same aim applies in the following method for describing chelate ring structures, which are rings that are formed by polar molecules coordinately linked to a central "chelated" metallic atom.

RULE 35 Delineate chelate structures by first citing the ring-forming molecules, then the central chelating atom, inside the parentheses. Cite coordinately linked open-chain side groups outside the parentheses, without locants. Three monocyclic and three bicyclic examples are illustrated below:

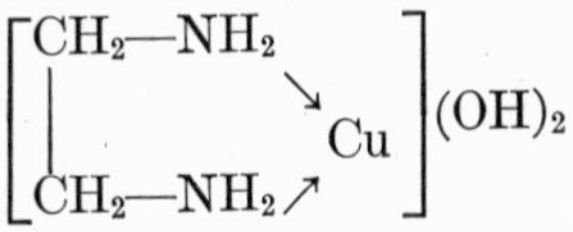

$$\left[\begin{array}{c} CH_2-NH_2 \\ | \quad\quad\quad \searrow \\ | \quad\quad\quad\quad Cu \\ CH_2-NH_2 \nearrow \end{array}\right](OH)_2 \qquad \left[\begin{array}{c} O \\ \diagup \quad \diagdown \\ O:C \quad\quad Co(NH_3)_4 \\ \diagdown \quad \diagup \\ O \end{array}\right](Cl)$$

(Z2ZCu),.Q₂   (OVOCo)Zh₄,.G

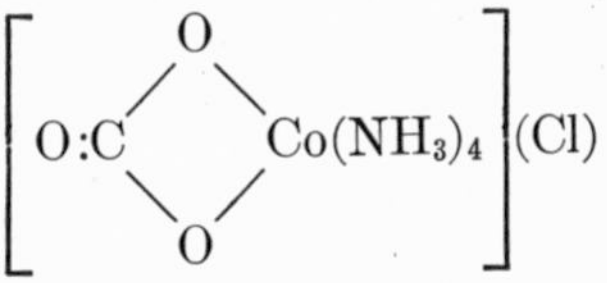

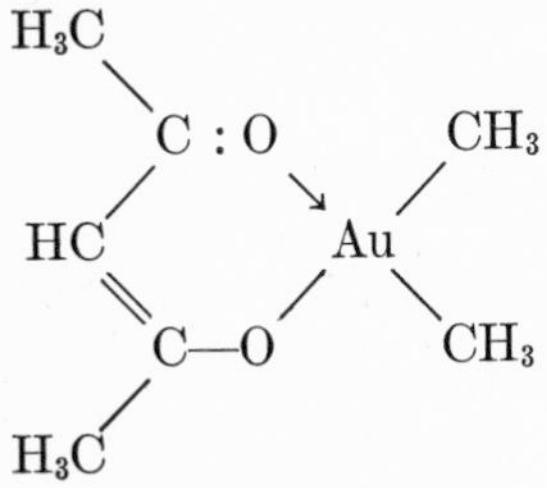

(OY.:1Y:OAu)1.1   (MSWM²Rh)QhQh.,Na

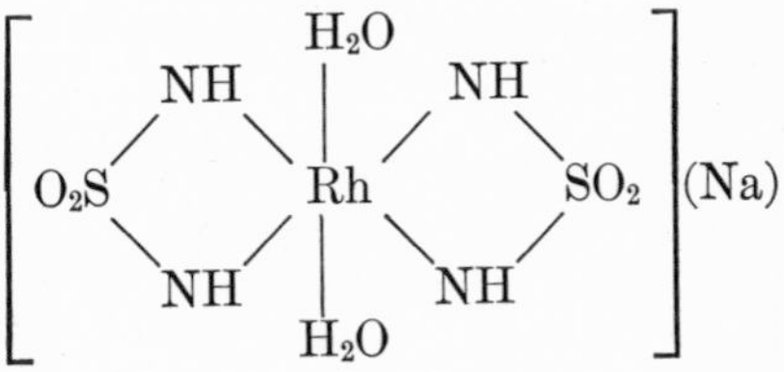

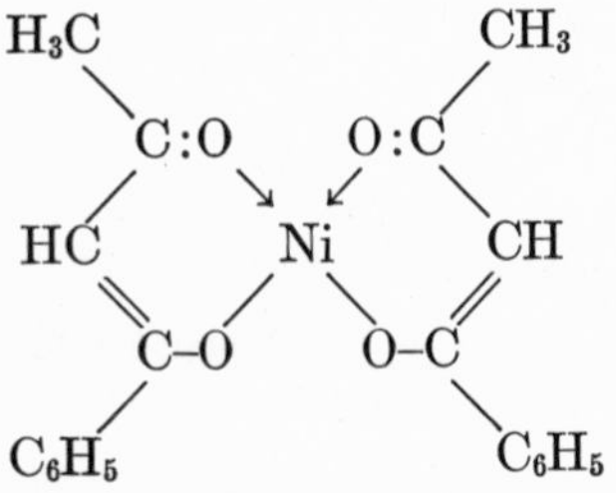

(OYR.:1Y:O²Ni)   (Z2Z²Cr)QQh,.G₂

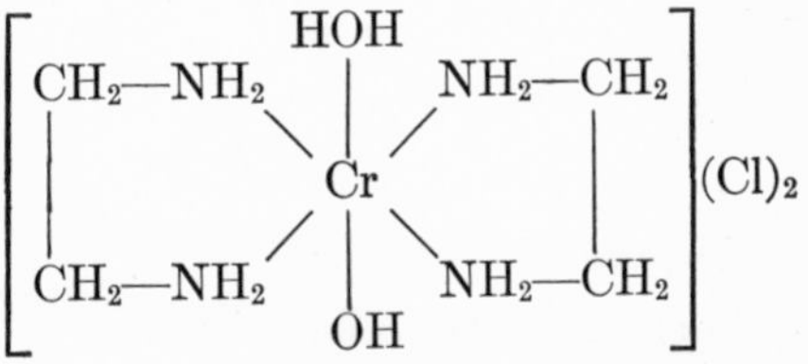

Note that the coordinately linked :O— atoms are not regarded as parts of simple carbonyl units, but rather as trivalent connectives. Note also the invariant definitions of G for Cl, M for NH, R for the benzene ring, V for —CO.—, W for nonlinear O₂, Y for the aliphatic ternary C atom, and Z for NH₂. These constantly used atomic group symbols are the unchangeable, irreducible "elements" of this line-formula notation.

36. THE CLASSIFYING PREFIX MARK (OPTIONAL)

Chemical structures are classified most usefully according to primary divisions such as Organic and Inorganic Realms, with subclasses associating Aliphatic Compounds, Carbocyclic Compounds, Heterocyclic Compounds, Covalent Inorganic Molecules, and Ionic Inorganic Salts. These traditional associations are maintained by prefixing a single-column *auxiliary* classifying mark to each description.

RULE 36   Use the following identifications in the first space of a "fixed column" tabulation to classify the fundamental types of structures:

a —   A blank space for aliphatic
        compounds; e.g.,   Q1YQ1Q   for glycerol

b —   A zero (nonprinting) for ben-
        zene derivatives; e.g.,   ØQVROV1   for aspirin

c —   A superscript or prime mark
        indicating the number of rings   '(6.N)   for pyridine
        (up to nine or more) in the ring   "(66.cN)   for quinoline
        system description which im-   *(c666)   for anthracene
        mediately follows*; e.g.,   #(666b6")   for pyrene

d — A comma for covalent inorganic
        compounds; e.g.,   ,ZZ   for hydrazine

e — A letter for inorganic salts; e.g.,   Na,.Q   for caustic soda
     or for nondescriptive formulae; e.g., As_2S_3 for orpiment

Additional structure-classifying prefix marks and indexing measures are mentioned briefly in Appendix D. Detailed explanations of these supplementary sorting and searching devices are beyond the scope of this manual.

* On the limited tabulating keyboard, the parentheses are denoted as LJ for carbocyclic compounds, or as TJ for heterocyclic compounds. Thus the second punched-card mark distinguishes heterocyclic from carbocyclic compounds, when this is desired.

PROMINENCE OF ACYCLIC, MONOCYCLIC, AND BICYCLIC STRUCTURES IN NRC TEST LIST

21.7 per cent contain no ring structures (acyclic or aliphatic compounds)

30.2 per cent contain only benzene rings (Chapter 7)

20.9 per cent contain other monocyclic systems (Chapter 8)

19.4 per cent contain bicyclic systems, and smaller systems (Chapter 9)

5.8 per cent contain tricyclic and smaller ring systems

1.4 per cent contain tetracyclic steroid (fused ring) systems

Only $\underline{0.6}$ per cent contain other tetracyclic and larger ring systems

100.0 per cent represent 30,000 biologically tested compounds

PROMINENCE OF FUSED SYSTEMS IN THE "RING INDEX" CATALOG OF LARGE RING SYSTEMS

TOPOLOGICAL DESIGNATION		NUMBER OF EXAMPLES IN "RING INDEX" CATALOG						
Symbol	Name	4-Ring Systems	5-Ring Systems	6-Ring Systems	7-Ring Systems	8-Ring Systems	Higher Systems	Sub-Totals
I. *Fused Systems* (Approximately 76 per cent of the tetracyclic and higher systems)								
A.	Angulinear	345	281	42	53	4	9	734
B.	Branched	46	37	39	48	5	6	181
C.	Condensed, Singly	105	80	37	11	4	1	238
D.	Doubly Condensed	29	48	40	27	10	4	158
E.	Polycondensed	—	6	13	11	9	13	52
II. *Other Systems*								
K.	Quaternary-fused	2	5	2	3	2	0	14
S.	Spiro	87	55	31	15	5	4	197
U.	Endobridged	70	30	18	6	0	0	124
W.	Endocyclic Bridged	—	7	6	11	1	2	27
Z.	Rings of Rings	10	25	1	4	0	9	49
"Polar Bond" Systems			13	6	0	0	0	19
Totals, by ring multiplicity		694	587	235	189	40	48	1793

Tricyclic and smaller systems comprise more than 2200 entries in the "Ring Index."

REVIEW EXERCISES

1. Draw diagrams for the following carbocyclic structures that were illustrated in this chapter. (Answers are given on the indicated pages.)

₃(567m′)	p. 107	(6/5/7L/″)	p. 107
(5,e6,h7)	111	(6/5/7k/*)	107
(5,e7,i6)	111	(6/7′5L′)	110
(5/6/7L/″)	107	(b567)	101
(6′6′b6i″)	110	(b576)	101
(6″7,i5)	103	(b5/6″7k″)	107
(6/5/7n/)	107	(b657)	101

$_3$(c567)	p. 101
(c576)	101
(c6/7,k5)	103
(d6/7′5)	103
$_4$(3/4/4/b4f/*)	109
(556b6n″)	109
(565b6n″)	109
(656b5n″)	109
(b5g565)	106
(b5g566)	106
(b5/g5/6/6/)	106
(c6566p′)	107
(c6665p/′)	107
$_5$(4/4/4/b4/c4h/#)	109
(d5665b6r″)	p. 113
(d5b6656r″)	113
(g7d6c665)	112
$_6$(5/4/4/b4/c4/d4j/^{5})	109
(aaab$_1$bc6u^4)	115
(dd$_1$caaa6w″)	115
(ebaaac6w*)	113
(ecaaab6w*)	113
(ecbaaa6w*)	114
$_7$(aaabcde6x^6)	114
(e4c5676b$_1$5b6v#)	111
$_{10}$(aaabcdeghi6f′.^{10})	114
$_{12}$(caaabde$_1$efgik6k′.^{12})	115

2. Draw diagrams for the following heterocyclic structures (pages 103, 104, 106, 107, 108, 110):

^{3}(b656.hM)
^{4}(b3/5/6′5k/′cMhO)
(b5g666.dS)
(b6/h6/6/6/NgNmN)
(c5/6/66p/′dMnOV)p:1
^{4}(c6b5/6/6.LO)—efjoQ$_4$
(c6/6/56p′gNLMh:c)eVMY1Qg
(d6b6/6/6.kN)
(e6c666.bVN)
^{5}(e6c5666t′dNkNV)
^{5}(f6d5c6/6/6.bN:eMoNV)
^{6}(g6e5d6/665w/′fM)
(g6/e5/d6/b5/5/6/N)giQLpr
(i5g6d6/b665.dK—jLvxO$_4$),.Q
$_7$(f5k5e6d6665z/′gSLVOV)

APPENDIX A

GENERAL CONSIDERATIONS FOR A CHEMICAL NOTATION

1. HISTORICAL DEVELOPMENT OF CHEMICAL SYMBOLS

Post-Alchemical Symbols

The earliest truly "elemental" symbols were the pre-atomic graphical characters devised by Hassenfratz and Adet; these appeared as an appendix to the *Nomenclature Chimique* of Lavoisier, Morveau, Fourcroy, and Berthollet (Paris, 1787). Among their several sets of symbols for substances of various kinds, these two writers included *encircled* letters to indicate *the presence of* metallurgical elements — such as an encircled A for "argentum," and As for "arsenicum."

About 20 years later John Dalton included their encircled C and Z symbols along with his other graphical symbols to denote *an atom of* copper or zinc, respectively. Dalton's pictorial symbols for atoms of other elements soon fell into disuse, probably because drawing them required too much writing effort.

Simple Letter Symbols for Atoms

The first truly *atomic* symbols were the unadorned letter symbols introduced by William Higgins in the marginal or inset diagrams of his treatise on the fallacy of the phlogiston theory.* Like modern structure-picturing chemists, he felt "obliged to introduce several diagrams, in order to render what I meant to convey the more intelligible; and indeed I thought it the surest mode of reasoning, and the most effectual means to come at truth." Higgins generally used capital letters to symbolize his "ultimate particles," such as C for copper, I for iron, M for mercury, S for sulfur, etc., and he drew lines (atomic valence bonds) between the letters to identify the "forces of attraction subsisting between the different kinds of ultimate particles and atoms of matter to each other."

* W. Higgins, *Comparative View of the Phlogistic and Antiphlogistic Theories*, 1789.

J. J. Berzelius, the "organizer of the science," started to systemize all chemical notation when he introduced the modern atomic letter symbols (1811–1819). Four of his scores of symbols were lengthened to improve their identity (e.g., L to Li and R to Rh), but none have been shortened up to the present time. The fact that only two (Cl and Br) are used often enough to justify shortening is a tribute to the keenness of his letter selections. Yet, "the admirable system of notation which Berzelius recommended met with violent opposition from many chemists, especially in England. People spoke of 'abominable symbols' which were more calculated to introduce confusion than clearness." *

Letter Symbols for Atomic Groups

Compound radicals or atomic groups have had letter symbols like those for the simple (atomic) radicals, ever since the atomic symbols were standardized. Thus the first known compound radical, the cyano or CN group, was denoted as Cy soon after its discovery by Gay-Lussac in 1815. The symbol Ae was used for the "aethyle" radical (C_2H_5) introduced by Dumas in 1828, but this later became Et (ethyl). The Bz symbol is still used for the benzoyl radical (C_6H_5CO.—) introduced by Liebig and Wöhler in 1832, and Ac— though it conflicts with an atomic symbol — still is used to denote the acetyl radical (CH_3CO.—) introduced by Liebig in 1839. The symbol Ad was used by Gregory and others in 1845 to denote the amido or amino NH_2 group, since Am generally was used to denote the ammonium or NH_4 group.

Auguste Laurent, in his famous *Methode de Chemie* (1853), denoted the hydroxyl group with the letter E ("eurhyzene"), describing the structure of water as HE and peroxide of hydrogen as E^2. He denoted the nitro group with the letter X, hence peroxide of nitrogen as X^2, and denoted the nitroso group as Y. These superscript multipliers, however, were not as lucid as Laurent's earlier (1846) representation of gaseous reactions, such as:

$$(HH) + (ClCl) = (HCl) + (HCl)$$

* Ernst von Meyer's "History of Chemistry," page 247, London, 1906. Berzelius showed less insight when he mutilated his neat and simple letter symbols with overmarked dots, commas, minus signs, or plus signs to show the number of combined oxygen, sulfur, selenium, or tellurium atoms, respectively; and with symbol-crossing bar marks to indicate doubling of the atomic unit. If these were the actual details that prompted the remarks about "abominable symbols," the criticisms certainly were justified!

The hydroxyl group also was denoted as *Hd* in Loschmidt's *Chemische Studien* (1861), and as *Ho* in Frankland's notational contributions (1866). These and Frankland's similar recommendations such as *Hs* for the mercapto group and *Ko* for the postulated KO group saved little if any writing effort, whereas his symbols Me, Et, Pr, and Bu for the first four alkyl hydrocarbon groups gained a lasting popularity.

Around 1852 dozens of lesser known and more complex organic radicals had been denoted with similar two-letter symbols — such as Ci for cinnamyl, Ct for cetyl, Fo for formyl, Gl for glyceryl, Sa for salicyl, and Ul for uryl. Inorganic atomic symbols were duplicated in casual assignments such as Ag for angelicyl, Ca for capronyl, Co for cocyl, Cr for caprinyl, Er for erucyl, Li for lipinyl, Mg for margaryl, Mo for moringyl, and Se for sebacyl. These scores of symbols for compound radicals soon fell into disuse, most likely because they were structurally unrevealing and statistically unimportant. *More effort was required to remember their meanings than was saved by writing symbols.* The total writing and remembering effort is minimized only when the new symbols have virtually self-evident meanings (such as numbers for numerical measures), or when the new symbols are used so frequently that such common usage serves as a constant reminder of their meanings. Thus the selection of each atomic-group symbol requires statistical as well as historical justification.

2. NEW SYMBOLS FOR PROMINENT ATOMIC GROUPS

The atomic groups and radicals that are most prominent in the chemical literature are combinations of just four elements — carbon, hydrogen, oxygen, and nitrogen. The outstanding dominance of C, H, O, and N atoms in structure descriptions is proven by the following figures, representing a ten-year sampling (1942–51) from *Chemical Abstracts* Formula Indexes:

96% of the compounds contain H atoms
95% contain C atoms
86% contain O atoms
64% contain N atoms
Only 28% contain S atoms
15% contain Cl atoms
10% contain Br atoms

No other element is present in more than three per cent of the listed compounds; thus these figures also furnish justification for the shortened halogen symbols.

The dominance of C, H, O, N, and S or halogen compounds suggests a very simple yet natural subdivision of formula-index classes:

16% of the compounds contain only C, H, and O atoms (three or less elements)

27% of the compounds contain N with the above (four or less elements)

25% of the compounds contain S with the above (five or less elements)

19% of the compounds contain halogens with the above (nine or less elements)

13% of the compounds contain the remaining *eighty-nine* elements

A more detailed analysis of complete structure descriptions (from the 30,000 biologically tested compounds that were cataloged at the National Research Council's Chemical-Biological Coordination Center, and were sampled for the IUPAC test list) shows that the four most prominent elements occur as follows:

Carbon atoms occur as

(1) simple CN—, NC—, OCN—, SCN—, etc., functions

(2) ternary aliphatic points, as in isopropanol

(3) quaternary aliphatic points, as in neopentane

(4) benzene rings (Present in about 50% of all compounds)

(5) alkyl chains or other cyclic segments

Oxygen atoms occur

(1) with carbon, as the carbonyl —CO.— connectives

(2) as oxy —O— units in ethers and esters; or as oxo O: units in aldehydes and ketenes

(3) as hydroxyl HO— groups in alcohols, phenols, and acids

(4) as nonlinear (physically branched) dioxo O_2 groups; e.g., in nitro —NO_2 terminals or sulfonyl —SO,— connectives.

Nitrogen atoms occur as

(1) dehydrogenated or "lone" N atoms (tertiary amines, etc.)

(2) monohydro or NH groups (secondary amines, etc.)

(3) dihydro or NH_2 groups (primary amines, etc.)

(4) cationic "lone" N atoms (quaternary amines)

These distinctive and most prominent types of C, H, O, and N groups led to the selection of arabic numerals for the alkyl chains or corresponding ring sizes, and nine new letter symbols (Y, X, R; V, Q, W; M, Z, K) for the remaining types itemized above. The symbols H, C, O, and N obviously serve best when they are reserved with their original meanings, as single atoms of these elements.

The value of mnemonic aids is recognized in the pictorial correspondence between the shape of the K, V, X, and Y letters and their bond patterns; the W suggests a "double O" or dioxo group related to the monoxo group in the very common divalent carbonyl connective. The letter M is taken from *imino* or *mid-amino*, Q from *aqua*, R from *regular-hexagonal resonating ring*, and Z from *hydrazine*. Finally, the two new halogen symbols G and E are taken from the word *halogen*, and provide an alphabetically compact set of halogen and hydrogen symbols (E to I). The letter G — the seventh letter in the alphabet — also avoids the objectionable typewriting ambiguity in the conventional Cl symbol of this seventh-group element.

3. ORIGIN OF THE "LINE–FORMULA" METHOD

In 1860, at the first International Chemical Congress held at Karlsruhe,* the leading chemists of the world met to resolve their confusions about atoms, molecules, radicals, and equivalents. Cannizzaro's famous clarification (and his insistence that there was only *one* correct set of atomic weights) immediately led to an extension of the primitive "theory of compound radicals" and to a realization that molecules generally are characterized by definite atom-to-atom linkages. Alexander Butlerow, who was the first to speak of the *structure* of a molecule, predicted in 1860 that the future work of the chemist would be to determine the manner of the mutual linking of the atoms in a molecule. Ever since this first recognition of structural importance, chemists have identified the molecular configurations in text copy simply by delineating the symbols for the corresponding molecular segments, one after another as connected. These are the "line-formula" descriptions.

Josef Loschmidt led this new era of structural chemistry with his publication of *Chemische Studien* (Vienna, 1861), which contained 368 remarkably astute graphical diagrams, including scores of benzene ring postulations. His text included a few "rationelle Formel"

* A list of references relating to the historical developments is given at the end of this appendix.

or line-formula descriptions, such as C_2H_5,O,C_2H_5 for diethyl ether; C_2H_5,O,CH_3 for ethyl methyl ether; and C_2H_5,O,C_2H_4,O,C_2H_5 for the glycol diethyl ether. In 1863 L. Carius denoted methyl alcohol as $CHHH,O,H$; and a year later, Emil Erlenmeyer denoted normal propyl alcohol simply as C_3H_7OH.

In 1866 August Kekulé, Henry Debus, and H. L. Buff popularized this line-formula technique with scores of lucid descriptions such as $CH_3.CO.CH_3$, $CH_3.CH_2.CO.CH_3$, H_3C—CO—OH, NC—CH_2—CO_2H, and H_2N—CH_2—CH_2—CO_2H. Unsaturation marks and ring-closing marks also were introduced by Erlenmeyer in this year 1866. The L or J shape of his ring-closing marks suggested the present author's use of parentheses to "enclose" the complete description for all ring systems except the simple benzene ring. Buff and Kekulé represented the phenyl radical in an unembellished manner that remains familiar to this day, as in C_6H_5—CH_2—CH_3, C_6H_5—CH_2—Br, $C_6H_5.CO.Cl$ and $C_6H_5.SO_2.OH$. Kekule further explained polysubstituted benzene ring isomers with *lower-case letter* symbols for the positions, as illustrated in Chapter 7 (page 65).

A summary of notational traditions, from William Higgins' atomic symbols of 1789 to the current Brand-Edsall symbols for polypeptide units, reveals that *letter* symbols always have been reserved to denote atomic groups, while punctuation marks — such as colon and period — have been reserved to denote modes of connection or disconnection. These symbols have been sequenced in a graphically direct manner, describing the structures from one end to the other, ever since the patterns of connection were postulated. In this present systemization of the line-formula method, the most frequently cited structure segments are represented by single marks, and all rarely encountered atomic groups are "spelled out" in full. In all further considerations, such as the selection of easily-remembered new symbols, the foremost guiding aim is the "Principle of Least Effort," a long-neglected natural law which George Kingsley Zipf revealed in 1949 as a fundamental pattern of action (or inaction!) that motivates all living behavior.

REFERENCES

LOSCHMIDT, J., "Chemische Studien," Vienna, 1861 (Ostwald Klassiker); also *Ber.*, **35**, 539 (1912); *J. Chem. Education*, **22**, 383 (1945).

CARIUS, L., *Ann. Chemie*, **126**, 195 (1863).

ERLENMEYER, E., *Ann. Chemie*, **126**, 306 (1863).

KEKULÉ, A., *Ann. Chemie*, **137**, 130–196 (1866); "Lehrbuch der Organischen Chemie," Erlangen, 1866, Vol. 2, pp. 499–512, 528.

DEBUS, H., *J. Chem. Soc.*, 1866, pp. 17–30, 256–289.

BUFF, H. L., *Ann. Chemie*, **140**, 156 (1866); "Grundlehren der Theoretischen Chemie," *Ann. Chemie, Suppl.* No. 4, p. 159 (1866).

FRANKLAND, E. AND B. F. DUPPA, *Ann. Chemie*, **138**, 328–360 (1866).

ERLENMEYER, E., *Ann. Chemie*, **137**, 339–354; **139**, 224–233 (1866).

BRAND, E., *Ann. N.Y. Acad. Sci.*, **47**, 187 (1946); *Ann. Rev. Biochem.*, **16**, 224 (1947); *Biochem. J.*, Suggestions to Authors, p. 3 (1949).

ZIPF, G. K., "Human Nature and the Principle of Least Effort," Addison-Wesley Press, Inc., Cambridge, 1949.

WISWESSER, W. J., *Aslib Proceedings*, **5**, 137 (1953).

4. THE INTERNATIONAL DESIDERATA

Simplicity of usage is the prime requirement of a good structure-describing notation, and is the first of the desiderata cited by the Coding Commission of the International Union of Pure and Applied Chemistry (IUPAC). This present notation achieves simplicity by incorporating the familiar symbols and delineating methods (outlined in the preceding appendix) as much as possible. Only eleven new letter symbols need be memorized, and all of these have mnemonic associations with the atomic groups that they represent. Structures are described from end to end, thus eliminating the need for position-identifying symbols and rules for tens of thousands of open-chain compounds and phenyl derivatives.

Ease of printing and typewriting, along with the closely related *ease of manipulation by machine methods*, are implicit in simplicity of usage. In line with these desiderata, the symbols in this notation were limited to those on the keyboard of a standard typewriter, and very simple translations suffice to fit the more limited keyboard of standard tabulating equipment. The general avoidance of subscripts, superscripts, and special marks in the present system facilitates rapid typing, easy printing, and accurate proofreading. Moreover, the eleven new letter symbols and size-indicating numerals supplement the established atomic symbols in such a way that all of the symbols of the tabulating keyboard are used as efficiently as possible. Finally, the initial citation of functional groups rather than alkyl or phenyl groups, and of characteristic nonbenzenoid ring systems rather than ring branches, facilitates structure searches with multiple-column selecting devices that scan punched cards at high rates of speed.

Instant recognizability, or comprehension at a glance, is one of the IUPAC desiderata. Since structures are described in this notation with graphical directness whenever possible, the resulting "typewriter pictures" are recognized at a glance. This attribute obviously is most important with unfamiliar structures — such as ICCF, NCCCCN, NCSCN, NCSI, O:NOF, and SCCCS. The familiar chain-picturing method illustrated with these relatively simple examples is extended in this notation to branched and cyclic structures of all degrees of complexity. New atomic group symbols have been assigned only to denote very common structural components; hence these new symbols, through their constant use, also become instantly recognizable. The conciseness of these symbol combinations also enhances recognizability, since fewer marks need be comprehended.

Exhibition of associations (*descriptiveness*) is contained to a perfect degree only in the space models of three-dimensional structures. Graphical diagrams, being virtual "letter shadows" of the molecule, give the next best descriptions, and the only ones that can be carried by printing or recording equipment. Two-dimensional diagrams of extensively branched structures can be typed or tabulated with the symbols of this notation, and these "unfolded delineations" retain a close similarity with the systematic linear descriptions.

Compatibility with accepted practices of inorganic chemical notation is important from the learning and teaching standpoint, since all branches of chemistry stem from general inorganic chemistry. This notation describes both organic and inorganic structures with the same symbols and methods, and in a manner that retains the "familiar look" of examples such as FF, NCH, OC, ON, ONO, and OSO. Equally appealing to teachers and students is the logical symbolism of this notation: capitalized letters for atomic groups, numbers for *absolute* measures, lower-case letters for *relative* positional values, and punctuation marks for modes of connection.

Conciseness was the third of the IUPAC desiderata, and the first such consideration mentioned by G. M. Dyson in his 1949 monograph. Concise yet exact descriptions facilitate recognizability, and inevitably reduce the copying or translating errors to a minimum. Conciseness is essential for the efficient use of tabulating machinery, since the information-carrying punched cards have a limited descriptive capacity. Even with new machines, card punching and verifying will remain the most expensive of the tabulating operations, and this processing cost is almost directly proportional to the number of descriptive symbols required. Therefore, conciseness means real economy in practical applications. The extreme conciseness of this notation is revealed by Dr. H. S. Nutting's data * on the average number of symbols required by each of four competing systems for the 650 randomly selected compounds in a "Beilstein" test list:

System	Symbols per Compound	Graphic Values
Dyson	27.45	×××××××××××××××××××××××××××.
Gruber	29.00	×××××××××××××××××××××××××××××
Silk	19.36	×××××××××××××××××××
Wiswesser	12.93	×××××××××××××

Conciseness alone is not very important, but the straightforward line-formula method that led to simplicity of usage, ease of typewriting, ease of manipulation by machine methods, and descriptiveness, also yielded this least disputable mathematical measure of notational brevity.

Uniqueness, the attribute of having one and only one correct symbol sequence for each structure, takes on added importance when the notation is to be used for indexing and classifying purposes. Familiar and infinitely extensible sequences such as numero-alphabetic order were used in this notation as much as possible to insure uniqueness. In this same aim, the rules were designed to make the starting point instantly clear for the vast majority of compounds.

Generation of an unambiguous and useful enumeration pattern is an indispensable requirement for satisfactory descriptions of cyclic structures, since these have no self-evident end-to-end sequences. The requirement has been met in this notation, first, by the use of a relatively simple yet all-inclusive procedure for determining positional relations in ring systems of all kinds; and second, by the use of distinctive lower-case letters to locate these relative positions. Open-chain structures have a fundamentally different topological nature; the lack of enumeration symbols in the long-enduring line-formula descriptions should be self-evident proof that enumeration patterns are not necessary, nor particularly useful, in acyclic structure descriptions.

* *Chem. Eng. News*, **30**, 410 (1952).

Ability to deal with partial indeterminants is a desirable feature of a truly universal notation. The simpler a system, the easier it is to provide a variety of symbols for the several kinds of uncertainties. In the present notation, half a dozen upper-case letters are available to symbolize generic atomic groups, such as J for halogen and A for any alkyl group. The lower-case letters x, y, and z are used for unspecified positions in small ring systems. The sharp mark ♯ suffices to identify labeled atoms, regardless of isotope values; and the question mark identifies mixed or uncertain open-chain connections. Other types of uncertainties can be indicated with variations or combinations of such markings.

The ability to generate a unique chemical nomenclature recalls the first thought and first rule of the International Union's Liége Conference of 1930: "As few changes as possible will be made in terminology universally adopted." Trivial names have remarkable survival vigor in spite of the official efforts made to promote the use of systematic names. For example, the following ten main entry names in the latest *Merck Index* (1952) appeared in William Gregory's *Outlines of Organic Chemistry* (1846): acetal, acetone, acetic acid, aconitic acid, acrolein(e), adipic acid, alcohol, alizarin(e), allantoin(e), and alloxan. These are less than half of the century-old names that begin with the letter *a*. Since names such as these are so well established, the supplementing structure description is best given as a notation rather than a systematic name. Systematic prefixes and suffixes can of course show a direct (rather than inverted) correspondence with the present notation in examples such as *p*-aminobenzoic acid, azidomethane, arsenosobenzene, bromoacetone, 1-chlorobutane, iodosobenzene, nitrosodiethylamine, and *o*-nitrotoluene. Thus there seems to be no imperative need to generate a new and unfamiliar systematic nomenclature to supplement this notation.

APPENDIX B

ALTERNATE PROCEDURES FOR SPECIAL STRUCTURE TYPES

1. "DIRECTED BRANCH" SYMBOLS D AND L

Carbohydrate derivatives are of sufficient importance to justify the introduction of two auxiliary atomic group symbols, to improve the notational correspondence among the many aldose, furanose, and pyranose stereoisomers.

Aldose chains are favorably oriented according to Rule 2a, because the resulting descriptions start with the unchanging $HOCH_2$— end of the chain, and this end determines the D or L family.* Notational correlations between this preferred open-chain orientation and its cyclic counterparts are improved by the following rule.

RULE 25d Denote "dropped" CHOH groups with the letter D, "lifted" ones with the letter L, and cite these symbols exactly like the related keto symbol V.

Two lists of examples illustrate the open-chain applications:

D-erythrose	D-glucose diethyl acetal
Q1DD1:O	Q1DDLDYO2.O2
D-ribose	———diethyl thioacetal
Q1DDD1:O	Q1DDLDYS2.S2
D-xylose	———diethyl monothioacetal
Q1DLD1:O	Q1DDLDYS2.O2
D-glucose	———S-Et O-Me monothioacetal
Q1DDLD1:O	Q1DDLDYS2.O1
D-mannose	———phenylosazone
Q1DDLL1:O	Q1DDLY:NMR.1:NMR
D-fructose	D-fructose diethyl acetal
Q1DDLV1Q	Q1DDLXO2,O2.1Q
L-arabinose	———diethyl thioacetal
Q1LLD1:O	Q1DDLXS2,S2.1Q
L-sorbose	D-glucosamine
Q1LDLV1Q	Q1DDLYZ,1:O

RULE 25e Delineate all carbohydrate derivatives in the same direction as the open-chain aldose or ketose form.

Thus the D or L symbols identify the following permitted violations of Rule 2a: D-ribonic acid is Q1DDDVQ and D-gluconic acid

---

* Emil Fischer followed this same left-to-right progression in his horizontally oriented aldose descriptions of 1891. (See C. S. Hudson's "Historical Aspects," *Advances in Carbohydrate Chemistry*, Academic Press, Inc., New York, 1948, Vol. 3, p. 5). The conventional vertically oriented diagrams should be viewed *from the right side*, to see this relation.

is Q1DDLDVQ. The cyclic correlations become much less baffling when the following regularities are clearly understood:

The *last* CHOH group cited in the cyclic parentheses is D for the *alpha* forms and L for the *beta* forms. (The *alpha-beta* definitions are confused in the literature, so this configurational definition may not correspond with others.)

The *first* aldose CHOH group takes the opposite directional sign if it forms a cyclic CH_2OH branch, or a cyclic $CHOH.CH_2OH$ branch.

Some aldose-furanose-pyranose correlations are shown in the following two series:

D-xyloaldose	D-glucoaldose
Q1DLD1:O	Q1DDLD1:O
α-D-xylofuranose	α-D-glucofuranose
(5/OcLDD)b/1Q	(5/OcLDD)b/L1Q
β-D-xylofuranose	β-D-glucofuranose
(5/OcLDL)b/1Q	(5/OcLDL)b/L1Q
α-D-xylopyranose	α-glucopyranose
(6/OcDLDD)	(6/OcDLDD)b/1Q
β-D-xylopyranose	β-D-glucopyranose
(6/OcDLDL)	(6/OcDLDL)b/1Q

If C. S. Hudson's designations for the *alpha-beta* forms* is followed, the last CHOH group in a cyclic α-D-sugar has the same directional symbol as the corresponding group in a cyclic β-L-sugar. The β-D- and α-L-sugars match in the same way.

2. AMINO NAPHTHOL–SULFONATE (N:O:S) NUMBERS †

The commercially important amino-naphthol-sulfonic acids often are identified by the N—O—S order of the eight CH-positional numbers. Thus the description for Chicago Acid, 1-amino-8-naphthol-2,4-disulfonic acid, is shortened to 1:8:2,4-Acid. These N,O,S numbers can be separated by two periods and placed within the ring parentheses to form obvious numerical identifications — not only for the acids, but also for the azo or N-linked dyestuff segments. A zero must be used to denote the absence of hydroxy groups (and of amino groups, if the idea is extended fully):

* C. S. Hudson, *J. Am. Chem. Soc.* **60**, 1539 (1938).
† An optional symbolism for dye chemists.

(1.0.2)	Lambda Acid	(1.8.35)	B Acid
(1.0.25)	L & M Acid	(1.8.36)	H Acid
(1.0.27)	Kalle's Acid	(1.8.4)	S Acid
(1.0.3)	Cleve-3 Acid	(1.8.46)	K Acid
(1.0.36)	Freund's Acid	(1.8.6)	Gamma-1 Acid
(1.0.368)	Koch's Acid	(2.0.1)	Tobias Acid
(1.0.38)	Epsilon Acid	(2.0.36)	Amino-R Acid
(1.0.4)	Piria Acid	(2.0.37)	F Acid (3,7)
(1.0.46)	Dahl-II Acid	(2.0.48)	C Acid
(1.0.47)	Dahl-III Acid	(2.0.5)	Dahl-I Acid
(1.0.48)	Disulfo-S Acid	(2.0.57)	Amino-J Acid
(1.0.5)	Laurent's Acid	(2.0.6)	Broenner Acid
(1.0.6)	Cleve-6 Acid	(2.0.68)	Amino-G Acid
(1.0.7)	Cleve-7 Acid	(2.0.7)	F-1 Acid
(1.0.8)	Peri Acid	(2.0.8)	Badische Acid
(1.2.4)	1:2:4 Acid	(2.5.7)	J Acid (I Acid)
(1.5.7)	M Acid	(2.8.36)	RR (2R) Acid
(1.8.24)	Chicago Acid	(2.8.6)	Gamma-2 Acid

This distinctive notation can be extended to include N-free di-
hydroxy disulfonic derivatives such as the following:

(0.13.57)	Yellow Acid	(0.17.36)	A Acid
(0.15.37)	Red Acid	(0.18.36)	Chromotropic Acid

Indicate substitutions by following the N—O—S numbering
direction with the proper locants (b for the first, g for the fifth, etc.,
H-substituting positions):

(0.1.36)jG	Chloro-H Acid	(1.8.36)bMV1	Acetyl H Acid
(1.0.8)bMR	Phenyl Peri Acid	(2.8.6)cM2	Ethyl Gamma Acid
(2.0.7)cM2	Ethyl F Acid	(.18.24)jNW	Nitro-1:2,4-Acid

The last example illustrates the use of an initial period to prevent
ring-number ambiguities when more than one N atom is present, and
when *all* N positions are cited. The N-linking symbol is cited unless
the NH_2 group remains unchanged:

(.12.0.4)cN:NRd².,Na₂	(1.2.36)bN:N(1.0.4).,Na₃
Congo Red	Amaranth
(.17.8.24)iN:NR1d².,Na₄	(2.18.36)cN:NRdNW.,Na₂
Evans' Blue	Chromotrope 2B
(.17.8.36)iN:NR1d².,Na₄	(.12.0.36)bN:NRSWQdRdN:N(:12.0.36)
Trypan Blue	Trypan Red

The above six azo dye examples are taken from the *Merck Index* (6th edition, 1952), which should be consulted for the detailed structure diagrams. The last example shows how the period next to the substituted N position is changed to a colon within the second set of parentheses, to identify the azo-linking position. Otherwise a hyphen and *b* locant would have to be prefixed to this second ring description.

3. POLYCYCLIC STRUCTURE VERIFICATIONS

The simple specification for a *longest chain of ring positions* also yields concise and infallible verifications of polycyclic structure descriptions, in terms of the nonconsecutive bonds. There will be just one such bond, described by the nonconsecutive pair of locants, for each ring in the system. Thus the three aromatic 6,6,6-ring systems can be described with the same locant assignments in two ways:

$$
\begin{array}{ccccc}
d-e-f-g-h \\
|\quad\;\,|\quad\;\,| \\
c-b-a-j-i \\
|\quad\;\,| \\
m-L-k
\end{array}
$$

(666′)
(af aj mb)

$$
\begin{array}{ccccccc}
f-g-h-i-j-k \\
e-d-c-b-a-n-m-L
\end{array}
$$

(b666)
(bg aj an)

$$
\begin{array}{ccccccc}
f-g-h-i-j-k-L \\
|\quad\;\,|\quad\;\,|\quad\;\,| \\
e-d-c-b-a-n-m
\end{array}
$$

(c666)
(ch aj an)

The sequences of paired locants are put into a unique order through two simple steps:

1) Cite the pairs in ascending order of the *higher* member of each pair.

2) Cite the lower member of each pair first if this one also is the *lowest* locant in the ring.

A locant pair is punctuated with the stroke if the ring formed by that bond contains more than one saturated carbon atom; otherwise the pairs are set off by blank spaces.

The four noncondensed aromatic 6,6,6,6-ring systems are verified as follows:

(c6 b666)   (ch bk an ar)   (e6 b666)   (ej bk an ar)
(d6 b666)   (di bk an ar)   (e6 c666)   (ej cL an ar)

Each of these systems has 18 ring members (r is the 18th locant). Two condensed aromatic 6,6,6,6-ring systems, with 16 and 17 atomic members, are:

(666 b6″)   (af aj mb pc)   (c6666′)   (ch aj an qb)

The 22 possible hexagonally fused pentacyclic systems are associated among five distinct types:

     ten *simple* systems, each with 22 ring atoms
     two *branched* systems, also with 22 ring atoms
     six *singly* condensed systems, each with 21 ring atoms
     three *doubly* condensed systems, each with 20 ring atoms
     one *triply* condensed system, with 19 ring atoms.

The delineated structure verifications are given in the following table.

HEXAGONALLY FUSED, AROMATIC, PENTACYCLIC SYSTEMS

All contain eight ternary (3-coordinate) atoms in the structure.

NONCONDENSED SYSTEMS		CONDENSED SYSTEMS	
Notation	*Nonconsecutive Bonds*	*Notation*	*Nonconsecutive Bonds*
(dcbaa)	(di cL bo ar av)	(cakaa′)	(ch aj kp ar ub)
(ecbaa)	(ej cL bo ar av)	(caLaa′)	(ch aj Lq ar ub)
(edbaa)	(ej dm bo ar av)	(dakaa′)	(di aj kp ar ub)
(fcbaa)	(fk cL bo ar av)	(dcaaa′)	(di cL an ar ub)
(fdbaa)	(fk dm bo ar av)	(ecaaa′)	(ej cL an ar ub)
(fdcaa)	(fk dm cp ar av)	(edaaa′)	(ej dm an ar ub)
(febaa)	(fk en bo ar av)		
(gdbaa)	(gL dm bo ar av)	(daaab″)	(di aj an qb tc)
(gdcaa)	(gL dm cp ar av)	(dbaaa″)	(di bk an ar tc)
(gecaa)	(gL en cp ar av)	(aaaLk″)	(af aj mb Lq kt)
(cibaa)	(ch in bo ar av)		
(djcaa)	(di jo cp ar av)	(aaabc*)	(af aj mb pc sd)

Note that positions in the noncondensed systems continue to the v (22nd) locant, and that the unbranched notations among these have a descending sequence of locants. Also note the importance of citing the locants for the notation in correct order, thus distinguishing between the condensed (daaab″) and (dbaaa″) systems.

APPENDIX C

PRIME MARKS FOR METHYL CONTRACTIONS
(AFTER GRUBER)

Dr. W. Gruber, recently favoring "end-to-end" structure descriptions, submitted an attractive suggestion to *show* methyl groups on Y, X, and K segments by adding prime marks to these special symbols.* This distinctive priming provides a simple mechanical transition between the fully explicit notation that beginners prefer, and the fully contracted one that experienced workers prefer. The procedure can be specified as an amendment to Rules 8b–9b (Rule 8a specifies that an *initiating* methyl symbol never be omitted or altered):

RULE 8–AA   Denote suffixed methyl groups on Y, X, and K positions by adding prime marks to these letter symbols: use the *apostrophe* prime mark for one methyl group, the *ditto* mark for two, and the *asterisk* for three methyl groups. In punched card applications where conciseness is essential, omit any prime mark on the last branch symbol and replace all others by *periods* (the 37th character mark) in accordance with the original Rules 8–10.

Thus Y' is an absolute designation for $-C(CH_3)-$, Y'' for $-C(CH_3)_2$, X'' for a complete $-C(CH_3)_2-$ connective, X* for a $-C(CH_3)_3$ terminal, and so on.

Two dozen of the many applicable open-chain examples from 2729 compounds in the NRC–IUPAC Test List are given on page 140.

APPENDIX D

CLASSIFYING AND INDEXING PREFIXES
(AFTER GRUBER)

Rule 36 (page 120) defines an auxiliary prefix which classifies all notations according to the multiplicity of the largest ring system in the structure. Dr. W. Gruber thought that this ring-indexing

* W. Gruber, private communication to the author, December 19, 1953.

measure was not enough for general classification; he suggested that it be preceded by prefix marks, set off by a distinctive punctuation, which would show (1) the atomic symbol of the characteristic "chain" element or rare atom in the structure; and (2) the number of atoms in the longest acyclic carbon-to-carbon chain.* A concise compromise measure is described in this appendix.

Only 13 per cent of the compounds in *C.A.* Formula Indexes, and only 7 per cent of those in the NRC–IUPAC Test List, contain rare "heteroid" elements other than H, C, O, N, S, and the halogens. The multitudes of "common element" structures can be subdivided efficiently among eight dominating "chain-type" classes, as shown by this table:

No. in Class †	*Class Prefix*	*Definition of Class*
438	—)	Carbon-chain structures (specified by the longest chain measure).
152	O-)	Simple oxa-chains: C...O...C sequence with no carbonyl groups.
258	V-)	Carbonyl oxa-chains with only *one* carbonyl connective (V).
226	W-)	Poly-carbonyl oxa-chains (more than one carbonyl V group).
512	N-)	Simple aza-chains: C...N...C with no NH nor quaternary N.
522	M-)	Secondary aza-chains: C...NH...C sequence, no quaternary N.
123	K-)	Quaternary aza-chains: ternary in aromatic positions (K).
304	S-)	Thia-chain structures: C...S...C sequence of bonds.
3	I-)	Iodinium chains: C...I...C sequence with cationic iodine.
191	Na), P-),	then all remaining elements in alphabetic order.

Each symbol implies possible inclusion of any of the preceding components (e.g., a K-chain may also include M or N segments, but not S). If two rare elements occur in the same structure, the higher-ranking symbol is listed (Hg for As and Hg).

* W. Gruber, private communications, Sept. 1953–Jan. 1954.
† From 2729 compounds in the NRC–IUPAC Test List.

The classifying column reserved for the second letter of a rare atom symbol also is used with the single-letter "chain-type" symbols to denote the number of carbon atoms in the longest *acyclic* carbon skeleton (up to "nine or more"). If two columns are allowed for this chain-length number, the measure should indicate the number of atoms in the longest acyclic C...to...C *heteratomic* chain.* Three examples of each principal chain type are given below with the one-column *carbon skeleton* measure:

C–)	O–)	V–)
–2) GY'G	O3) 1X"O1OX *	V9) 1ØVOY"
3) NCX"G	O3) QY'1OY"	V3) F1VOY"
15) QVX'7.7	O4) QY'Y'O4	V6) QY'1OV5

W–)	N–)	M–)
W4) 2OVVX *	N3) 1Y'NV2.Y"	M3) 2OVMY"
W4) 4OVY'OVO2	N6) 1Y'NV4VO2.Y"	M4) E1VMY'2
W4) E1VVOY'2	N3) 2N2.VY'OV1	M4) ZVMVOY'Y"

K–)	S–)
K9) 1ØK *,.E	S8) G2OSO.OY'6
K5) 1OV2K *,.E	S5) QV1S1Y'1Y"
K2) OV1K *	S3) WS2.X"SW2

The "rare atom" prefix, while obviously not recommended with binary inorganic descriptions such as CuS, Fe_3O_4, MgO, NaF, and $ZnSe$ (or $CaCO_3$ and Na_3PO_4), also can serve to correlate the rarer metallic components among more complex ionic descriptions such as the following:

Ca)CC.,Ca	Ca)O$_4$As.,^{2}Ca$_3$/Qh^3	Na)ONO.,Na
B3)CCC.B$_{12}$	Ca)O$_7$B$_4$.,Ca	Na)ON:NO.,Na$_2$
Ka)EIE.,Ka	Si)O$_8$Si$_2$.,CaAL$_2$	Ba)OO.,Ba
Pt)G$_6$Pt.,H$_2$	Ca)OBO.,^{2}Ca/QH$_6$	Pt)Q$_6$Pt.,H$_2$
Pb)NNN.,^{2}Pb	Ka)OG.,Ka	Ba)S$_3$S.,Ba/QH^2

Inorganic salts, characterized by a *letter* in the first column of the structure description, cannot contain alkyl numerals; hence on punched cards, the *subscript* multipliers are shown without blank spaces. (Prefix sorting with IBM cards is facilitated by the fact that the prefix letters K and S, N and V, O and W have the numeric punches 2, 5, and 6, respectively.)

---

* Dr. Gruber later suggested (February, 1954) that some chemists would prefer to show the *total* carbon count in this alternate measure.

INDEXES

INDEX TO TABLES OF RADICALS

Obvious additive combinations are not entered here; see pages 8, 9, 13, 21, 22, 57, and 58 for such acyclic combinations, and pages 64, 66, and 69 for benzenoid combinations; see chemical name index for "root" names of all other cyclic radicals.

141

CHEMICAL NAME INDEX

Generic types are distinguished by italics.

GENERAL INDEX